THE ROYAL ACADEMY OF ENGINEERING

# Engineering for Sustainable Development

*What does society expect from engineers as it strives to improve human well-being without further environmental degradation?*

PROCEEDINGS OF A TWO DAY CONFERENCE TO EXPLORE
THE CHALLENGES AND OPPORTUNITIES FOR ENGINEERS
WITH ILLUSTRATIONS FROM MANUFACTURING AND TRANSPORT

*Edited by Dr James McQuaid FEng*

**21/22 SEPTEMBER 1995**
LONDON

*Engineering for Sustainable Development (Conference Proceedings)*

© THE ROYAL ACADEMY OF ENGINEERING

*Except pages 23-34* © Sir Robin Ibbs KBE
*and pages 47-50* © Rt Hon Ian Lang MP

ISBN 1 871634 45 8
*December 1995*

*Published by*
THE ROYAL ACADEMY OF ENGINEERING
29 Great Peter Street
Westminster
London
SW1P 3LW

*Telephone* 0171 222 2688
*Facsimile* 0171 233 0054

*The Royal Academy of Engineering is a Registered Charity (No. 293074)*

# Engineering for Sustainable Development
## Foreword

The Conference *Engineering for Sustainable Development* was a major event directed to gaining the participation and commitment of engineers towards the goal of Sustainable Development. The context for the conference is set out in the Opening Address by the President of The Academy, Sir William Barlow.

In organising the Conference, we set as one of our objectives the speedy publication of these proceedings including discussions. We are confident that they will provide an important statement of position for practising engineers and a valuable source of information for the education of the engineers of the future. We hope that the contents will instil a greater sense of what is expected of engineers and what they can contribute.

It is entirely appropriate that The Academy, with its objective of promoting the advancement of engineering for the benefit of society, should be at the forefront of the debate which will crystallise engineering's agenda for delivering Sustainable Development. In the proceedings, representatives from various sectors of society as well as industrial and academic practitioners provide valuable guidance on the components of a forward strategy that recognises the complex interactions between engineering and society's needs. There are many important messages contained both in individual papers and in panel discussions. Interweaved between the messages there are several recurring crosscutting themes which we would wish to identify for special emphasis. These are:

- To achieve the goal of Sustainable Development requires engineers to translate society's objectives into practicably realisable solutions. Engineers must take every opportunity to communicate to society at large the importance of the profession's contributions to the improvement of the quality of life for all on this planet through the achievement of technological progress. This must include raising their profile in determining national and international strategies and more generally in making themselves more visible as the prime movers in Sustainable Development initiatives form the shop floor to international fora.

- The international connections of engineers, through their companies and their professional bodies, provide an invaluable means for the rapid dissemination of good practice. The high standards applied in particular countries and in particular sectors of industry can provide a foundation for ensuring that the best becomes the good and the pace of Sustainable Development is thereby enhanced. Engineers have a particularly key role to play in driving the diffusion of technology and best practice from the developed to the developing countries.

- Related to that is the realisation that changes to practices in pursuit of Sustainable Development objectives are good for business. The market opportunities provided by the demand for technological, solutions will of themselves comprise a very significant factor in world trade, as emphasised by the President of the Board of Trade in his address. Businesses which fail to recognise that will lose out.

- The recognition of the distinction between Clean Technology and Sustainable Development is of crucial importance. Engineers are already in the forefront in Clean Technology programmes of many kinds. The extension of the scope of Clean Technology to embrace the much more wide-ranging demands of Sustainable Development, for example the prudent use and reuse of materials and the minimisation of consumption of non-renewable energy sources, was emphasised as an essential concomitant of the way forward for engineers.

- The engineering design focus needs to move from fitness-for-purpose in various directions. Engineers have a proper part to play in reorienting society's definition of purpose in key areas such as transport. They need to adjust from a focus dictated solely by engineering rationality to recognise that social expectations now include considerations which lie outside the traditional quantifiable concerns of the engineer. Social priorities may not be measured by simple balance of economic costs and benefits. Engineers need to be fully involved in the framing of those expectations. In doing this, they need to work on enhancing the trust that the public can place in them, hopefully reverting to the position of public confidence enjoyed by the pioneering engineers of Victorian times in forging the industrial revolution and improving social conditions. A particular message was the close integration already achieved between health and safety requirements and functionality in the design of processes and products should be extended to include sustainability considerations.

A further tough underlying theme was that the timescale over which sustainability can be fully achieved demands that current profligacy in the use of resources has to be offset now by technological and intellectual investment. The results of this investment will provide a legacy from the present to future generations to help them cope with the reduced resources and environmental problems which they will inevitably inherit.

The conference built on a successful meeting in March 1994 *Signposting the Sustainable Development Strategy*, the proceedings of which were published in June 1994. The 1995 event provided a springboard for future Academy activities which could include a series of events on specific themes and initiatives of wider scope in education and in collaboration with Government. Through these activities, an understanding of the role of engineering in providing solutions to environmental problems should become embedded in the University and Further Education Systems, in the Continuing Professional Development programmes for engineers and in the process of forming national policies. It is through such activities that engineers will turn the vision of Sustainable Development into reality.

A conference such as this relies for its success on the willing co-operation of many people. We were fortunate in being able to attract so many distinguished speakers to give their time in preparing and presenting their papers. The value of the Conference was considerably enhanced by contributors to the discussions, of which we have included as much as space limitations would allow. We owe a particular debt to Stewart Miller CBE FEng, Professor Tony Ridley CBE FEng, Professor Roland Clift OBE FEng, Alec Silverleaf CB FEng and Sir Martin Holdgate CB for their part in arranging, managing and reporting on the individual sessions. Many of the staff of The Academy, led by Miss Christa Langan, gave us enormous assistance throughout. Dr Richard Judge CEng , on secondment from AEA Technology, acted as a most able facilitator and assistant to us on the Working Group throughout the preparations and contributed many useful ideas. Finally, the financial security of the Conference was assured by the generous assistance provided by our sponsors. To each and all, we are most grateful.

**Dr James McQuaid FEng** *Chairman*

**Dr Glyn England JP FEng**         **Dr Brian Eyre CBE FEng**
**Professor Anthony Kelly CBE FEng FRS**        **Sir John Knill FEng**

*The Royal Academy of Engineering Working Group on Sustainable Development*
*December 1995*

# Sponsors

THE ROYAL ACADEMY OF ENGINEERING
*wishes to acknowledge the generous support of
the following organisations for this conference
and the publication of the proceedings:*

AEA Technology

Department of the Environment

Rover Group plc

Rust International plc

UKCEED

# Engineering for Sustainable Development

## CONTENTS

THE ROYAL ACADEMY OF ENGINEERING

# Engineering for Sustainable Development

## SESSION ONE

### The Expectations of Society

**Chairman** Sir William Barlow FEng
**Rapporteur** Professor Anthony Kelly CBE FEng FRS


**The UK Strategy: Implications for Decision Makers**
Joan Ruddock MP

**The Challenges for Enterprise**
Sir Robin Ibbs KBE

**Consumers: the Neglected Dimension of Sustainable Development**
Dame Rachel Waterhouse

**The Ethical Input to Engineering Decisions**
The Right Reverend Richard Harries DD FKC

**Keynote Address** The Rt Hon Ian Lang MP

# Session One
# The Expectations
# of Society

**Chairman**

Sir William Barlow FEng
President, The Royal Academy of Engineering

## Personal Profile

**Sir William Barlow** was born in 1924, and educated at Manchester Grammar School and Manchester University, where he obtained a First Class Honours degree in Electrical Engineering. After graduating he spent three years in the Royal Navy. In 1947 Sir William began his industrial career with The English Electric Company where he spent 21 years, serving in management positions in Spain, Canada and England – his last as Managing Director of English Electric Computers, where he organised the merger with ICT to form ICL. In 1970 he was invited by the British Government to organise the merger of Britain's three major ball-bearing companies into RHP, of which he was Chairman and Chief Executive until 1977.

In 1977 he was appointed Chairman of The Post Office which then contained both the postal and the telecommunications services with 420,000 employees. In 1980 he organised its division into two separate corporations – The Post Office and British Telecom.

Sir William then returned to the private sector as Chairman of the THORN EMI Engineering Group until 1984.

From 1984 to 1992 he was Chairman of BICC Plc, which had £4 billion sales and 47,000 employees, of which 22,000 were in overseas subsidiaries. It is in cables, construction and communications.

Among his current business appointments he is a Director of Vodafone Group plc, Waste Management International plc, NBI Limited and Chemring Group plc.

He has been President of The Royal Academy of Engineering since 1991. He has Honorary Doctorates from Cranfield, Bath, Aston, City, Liverpool John Moores and Loughborough Universities. He is an Honorary Fellow of the Institution of Electrical Engineers, the Institution of Civil Engineers and the Institution of Mechanical Engineers and an Honorary Fellow of UMIST and London Business School.

He was President of BEAMA 1986-87, Master of The Worshipful Company of Engineers 1986-87, Chairman of The Design Council 1980-86, Chairman of The Engineering Council 1988-91 and President of ORGALIME 1990-1992.

# Opening Address
## Sir William Barlow FEng

## Introduction

I have great pleasure in welcoming you to our conference. I want to take just a few minutes to set the scene.

The 150 leaders who attended the 1992 Earth Summit declared their commitment to implement actions necessary to address Sustainable Development. The government responded to this in 1994, by publishing the White Paper setting out the UK's Strategy. This paper describes itself as the starting point in the national debate to make choices necessary for delivering sustainable development.

Despite considerable activity in the area, there is a wide perception of a lack of coherent engineering thrust in the debate so far compared, for instance, to that provided by economics and biology.

This underlines two fundamental needs:

- Firstly, we need to ensure that the *relevance* of the engineering contribution to sustainable development is fully understood and taken on board by both government and the wider public;

- Secondly, we need to emphasise the *importance* of this contribution within the engineering profession itself.

## Participation process

A product of the 1992 Earth Summit was a comprehensive programme of actions, summarised in Agenda 21. This includes the comment:

"One of the major challenges facing the world community, as it seeks to replace unsustainable development patterns with environmentally sound and sustainable development, is the need to activate a sense of common purpose in all sectors of society"

The key point is that society needs to agree the principles on which it will base its future development and accept that there will be associated costs. We need to define and agree priorities.

In making choices for Sustainable Development, there is a need to consider a mix of *tangibles*: such as scientific data and understanding , economic statistics, engineering application and practicalities and *intangibles*: such as ethics, consumer drivers, society's aspirations.

A key question is how the engineering contribution can be optimised. We can contribute more fully and effectively with a knowledge of what society can offer. I am therefore delighted that such a distinguished group of speakers has agreed to help guide us in our deliberations. I am looking forward immensely to hearing their views.

## Engineering's Contribution

We will hear much about innovation and the exciting opportunities for engineering during the conference. The Engineering Council Guidelines for the Environment quote a global market for environmental technologies of 200 billion dollars *today*, forecast to rise to 500 billion dollars within 15 years. British scientists and engineers who are adept at helping to reduce environmental problems whilst simultaneously increasing profits will be in strong demand.

Sustainable development is also a potential platform on which to build a more exciting future for engineering in the UK. By embracing sustainable development in a positive way we can both open up new opportunities for engineering creativity and enhance the attractiveness of the profession in the minds of young people.

In designing the programme for this conference, we recognised that a number of the key issues cut across industrial sectors: for example waste management, design, regulatory influences. The rapporteurs at this conference have a particular challenge to draw together such lateral issues. These are particularly important, as they allow the conclusions from the conference to have much broader application than just the two sectors of industry on which we have chosen to focus.

## Closure

The key message that I leave with you with is that technology has conferred enormous benefits on society in terms of quality of life. This is reflected in the high standards enjoyed by the industrialised countries compared to the developing world. But equally, we recognise that there have been penalties in terms of pollution, exhausting of resources and so on. A fundamental issue if we are to achieve sustainable development is how to minimise the risks of such penalties.

Finally, I would like to return to the White Paper defining the UK strategy. The Prime Minister's foreword highlights the need for "a hard headed approach to sustainability based on good science and robust economics". I agree... But equally important is the delivery of *practical* solutions. That is the role of the engineer, and it is a role that is fundamental to the success of any sustainable development policy. We must ensure that society recognises its importance.

# The UK Strategy:
# Implications for
# Decision Makers

**Joan Ruddock MP**

Opposition Spokesperson on
Environmental Protection

## Personal Profile

**Joan Ruddock** has been Member of Parliament for Lewisham Deptford since 1987. She is currently Opposition spokesperson on environmental protection having been previously a member of the shadow home affairs (1992-94) and transport (1982-92) teams. In 1989 she successfully piloted a Private Members Bill on the control of flytipping through the House of Commons.

She graduated in botany from Imperial College and before entering Parliament worked in housing, with unemployed young people and as the manager of a Citizen's Advice Bureau. She was Chair of the Campaign for Nuclear Disarmament from 1981-1985.

# The UK Strategy: Implications for Decision Makers

**Joan Ruddock MP**

## Introduction

The UK Strategy for Sustainable Development is of course a strategy devised by a Conservative government and must be recognised as such.

Its declared aim is to reconcile two fundamental aspirations: for continuing economic development to secure higher standards of living now and for future generations; and the protection and enhancement of the environment today and in the future.[1]

The language is important. The Labour Party's environment policy paper *In Trust for Tomorrow* uses the Brundtland definition which speaks of meeting needs rather than simply raising standards.

Even more expressive, in my view, is the definition "improving the quality of human life while living within the carrying capacity of supporting ecosystems".[2]

That, I think, should be the challenge for our government and for our global society. The nature of the challenge is not new. The hugely adverse environmental burdens of our industrial revolution are obvious to all – but our mistakes are still being repeated around the globe.

Post war reconstruction brought its own penalties and it took our sophisticated scientifically educated nations decades to respond to the warnings that 'modern' solutions such as pesticides carried their own poisonous legacy.

It is just eight years since the UN Report *Our Common Future*[3] warned world leaders of the severe consequences of continuing pollution and of the destruction of natural resources. Since then terms such as global warming, acid rain, soil erosion and desertification have dominated international environmental agendas.

Britain, along with the other highly industrialised nations of the world, bears a particular responsibility. We have been used to using more than our fair share of the raw materials of the world, and adding disproportionately to its huge environmental burdens.

Engineers have been in the vanguard of that assault on the environment, albeit, primarily, in the pursuit of improving human living standards.

So, what are the implications for decision-makers now that the concept of sustainability has been codified and what does society expect of engineers?

## Engineering, Science and Technology

I fear that 'society' would not recognise that it had any expectations of engineers. In evidence to the Education Select Committee's enquiry into *Science and Technology in Schools*[4], the Director General of the Engineering Employers Federation said 'unfortunately the traditional image of engineering is in the foundry or in the rather dirty workshop...'

I fear it may be even worse – engineers probably lack any identity in the mind of the average citizen. Yet people have always admired and been inspired by engineering triumphs – from the Ironbridge in Shropshire at the cradle of the industrial revolution; to our own Thames Barrage here in London; to the Channel Tunnel, realising the dream of so many to remake the land link between these islands and continental Europe.

Perhaps it is the very diversity of tasks undertaken by engineers which leads to such a lack of identity. Your different disciplines together impact on virtually every aspect of people's lives.

Yet it is already clear that your potential has been seriously undermined in recent years.

According to the Education Select Committee's report, already quoted, there has been a 'falling off' of interest and involvement in these subjects. Maths and science teaching is often poor, there is a lack of resources for technology teaching and expectations of children are too low. In the past fifteen years the proportion of graduates with degrees in engineering and technology has fallen from 14% to 12% for first degrees and 18% to 13% for higher degrees.

International comparisons tell their own story – in 1991 UK engineering graduates were 10.7% of the total, in Germany 18.8%, in Japan 22.8% of total graduates.

Even more depressing is the position of women in the engineering profession. Thanks to the huge efforts of the WISE (Women in Science and Engineering) campaign, the proportion of women studying engineering was raised from 7% in 1984 to 15% in 1994. But women still make up less than 10% of engineering and technology students in further education, even though engineering and technology is one of the largest sectors in further education.

This abject failure to recruit effectively from half the country's population needs to be urgently addressed.

Labour is currently consulting on 16-19 education with a view to broadening the curriculum and ensuring a better scientific education for all. We will specifically address gender imbalance.

At the heart of Labour's economic strategy is the determination to create a highly educated and highly skilled workforce. To this end our proposals include:

- lifelong learning, with new opportunities for retraining those in work

- a skills audit of the nation, enabling Britain to identify the skills in short supply with a view to targeting training resources

- a University of Industry, a public-private partnership, which will exploit new communications technology to bring the latest innovations in learning direct to the workforce.

We believe it is the failure to invest in capacity, both physical and human, which lies at the heart of Britain's inflation and slow growth problems. Britain still remains near the bottom of the league in spending on research and development, with repeated Government cuts undermining the efforts of industry to remedy the situation. Confidence continues to be eroded, with the Office of Science and Technology moved to its third department in three years, with four different ministers in the same period.

Labour will ensure that the OST genuinely co-ordinates a much needed government strategy on science. We intend to give a clear lead in transfusing society with a much deeper and broader sense of the importance of science, and make a long-overdue shift from short-termism to the implementation of longer-term economic, social and environmental goals.

We believe that this country's scientists and engineers are one of our key national assets and essential partners in our vision of the future. Without your contribution, environmentally sustainable development cannot be achieved.

## Labour's Programme for Sustainable Development

Labour in government will adopt a more comprehensive and imaginative approach to the environment than has been the British record to date. We will not be burdened by the present Government's ideological obsession with privatisation and deregulation or its antipathy towards the European Union – all of which undermine its own declared commitment to Sustainable Development.

Instead, four key themes will condition our thinking:

- the need to place the environment at the heart of all areas of policy
- recognition that effective environmental protection requires the whole range of government action and cannot rely on the free market
- a belief that high environmental standards drive economic efficiency
- recognition that environmental progress and social equity go hand in hand.

I do not underestimate the challenge we have imposed on ourselves in accepting these key themes. In seeking to apply environmental considerations across all areas of policy, we would make a considerable impact on the world of engineering. We will need to seek to do so in consultation and partnership.

## Economy

One of the greatest expectations people will have of an incoming Labour government is job creation and maintenance. Gordon Brown, in a recent policy document *Rebuilding the Economy*, set out an "economic programme which will lay the foundations for a cleaner and greener society in which protection of our environment is a priority". Each year in the run-up to the budget, Labour will publish a consultative green paper which will spell out the state of the economy, progress in achieving government objectives and a forecast for the coming year. Our measurement of economic performance will include new environmental indicators.

We propose a gradual transformation of the economy, setting standards, employing regulation and incentives, making public investment and private partnerships to ensure that economic development becomes more sustainable. We will require larger companies to report on environmental performance and strategy, so as to optimise resource use, reduce pollution and disseminate best practice.

We believe there is a huge and neglected potential for job creation and export success within the new environmental technologies in which, of course, engineers would play a key role. The OECD estimate that the world market for environmental technologies and services is currently worth $250 billion and predicted to reach $600 billion by the year 2000. Yet the 1993 Science White Paper *Realising our Potential*[5] said nothing about promoting environmental industries.

A recent survey of the small British environmental industry revealed that 89% believe the Government is not doing enough to support it.[6] The main areas of failure were identified as:

- not adequately enforcing environmental laws
- not providing investment incentives for mainstream industry
- not providing adequate R&D support for environmental entrepreneurs.

Labour intends to 'catch up' and will adopt a three point strategy to raise the domestic output in environmental technologies.

- We will set national targets for progress in the application of new technologies such as renewable energy and give businesses the confidence that there will be predictable growth in the domestic market.
- We will pursue public procurement policies which offer value for money and which meet environmental criteria such as low energy content.

And in the belief that environmental regulations are a spur to innovation and to the development of high quality products,

- We will ensure that Britain's environmental regulations match that of other nations.

We lag far behind our international competitors, many of whom have comprehensive environmental strategies aimed at capturing the new technology markets for their own industry. Over the next twelve months Labour will continue to consult with industry in more detail on these strategies. We also intend to seek to harness the enthusiasm of young people by creating an environmental task force to provide worthwhile work in the community.

## Sustainable Energy Policy

Consideration of economic policy leads us, inevitably, to another major engineering sector – energy generation. The relationship between energy use and economic development has changed fundamentally in recent years. The most dynamic economies, Germany and Japan, have pointed the way forward, by successfully decoupling economic growth from energy use. In Britain by contrast, the ratio of energy use to unit of GDP has worsened. The consequential continuing depletion of natural resources and multi-media pollution are obvious.

Labour – again with your help – will seek to implement a sustainable energy policy. It will be two-pronged – aimed simultaneously at reducing demand and developing cleaner energy supplies.

We believe Britain could make a greater contribution to the reduction of global warming gases and toxic emissions.

We will set a series of national targets for energy consumption. We believe significant energy savings could be made in a relatively short time-frame, both at the point of generation and in the domestic sector. We have proposed a self-financing national programme of energy efficiency work, with the linked objectives of combating fuel poverty, reducing carbon dioxide emission and generating substantial long term employment. We intend to make the Energy Saving Trust live up to its expectations.

We propose a changed regulatory regime for the energy industry, improved building regulations; minimum efficiency standards for appliances and energy efficiency programmes for local authorities.

We also intend to increase power station efficiency through combined heat and power schemes.

It is clear that much more could be done in the development of cleaner production and the use of renewables. We will end the scandal of a regulatory regime which penalises clean production such as has happened at the coal-fired Drax station.

Helping to meet environmental objectives is not the only merit in developing renewable energy technologies. There is undoubtedly a potential gain in regional development and employment, particularly in rural areas.

Whilst the environmental impact of energy generation has long been understood, far less attention has been paid, until recently, to the consequences of energy use in transport.

## Transport

Mrs Thatcher's 'great car economy' was pivotal in a philosophy of individualism, privatisation and deregulation. Today the massive burden of pollution arising from the relentless rise of road transport has become a matter of real public concern.

Whether that concern will be sufficient to support radical change only time will tell, but there is no doubt that we are systematically poisoning ourselves and our environment by toxic emissions from road transport.

Technical fixes are possible for individual vehicles and a Labour government would seek the fastest possible progress on clean vehicle technology and to the highest standards.

But no amount of technical fixing can solve the problems of congestion and the potential doubling of vehicles on our roads. Labour has long known and accepted that constraint.

Our aim will be to establish an integrated and sustainable transport system – a better balance between private and public, rail and road – in short, real choice aimed at persuading people to reduce car use. We will aim to encourage public transport provision and rail and water-borne freight.

Reordering national priorities is the business of government and achieving a sustainable transport policy into the 21st Century will be in everyone's interest.

The task is daunting. It will require not only public support but a dynamic partnership between central government, private industry and local authorities.

## Environmental Pricing and Economic Instruments

Any discussion of transport and the environment inevitably leads to consideration of the use of economic instruments.

Labour has long acknowledged the potential of eco-taxes in influencing behaviour. The success of the differential pricing of lead-free petrol has set an important precedent and there is undoubtedly much further scope for fiscal measures in the transport field, but Chancellors need to anticipate the wider effects of environmental taxes. The Government's VAT on fuel and landfill tax are good examples. Both, in our view, derive from the Government's need to raise revenue to compensate for failed economic policies, rather than to change behaviour in the interests of the environment. Both, as conceived, were fatally flawed. Thus VAT on domestic fuel took no account of social equity – a prime consideration for Labour. And the landfill tax as proposed to be collected on an ad valorum basis looked designed to increase the commercial advantage of cheap landfill sites, rather than reduce the use of landfill as intended.

The minimisation of waste production, reduction in the use of landfill, the recovery of energy from waste and the conservation of domestic energy are all aims of a Labour government. But if fiscal instruments are to be used in the attainment of those aims they will have to be more sharply focused and sensitive to the test of social equity.

## Urban and Rural Environment

It is that link between social equity and environmental protection that distinguishes Labour from other political parties. Nowhere is the link more obvious than in the built environment. The massive achievements of engineering in bringing sewerage, clean water, and new homes to millions of people post-war, have been eclipsed by the growing decay and huge inequalities between the living conditions of the very rich and the very poor in today's Britain.

Labour is committed to improving both our rural and urban environments, while preserving Britain's biodiversity.

This will require a strengthened and democratised planning system – about which we are currently consulting and where your input will be most welcome.

We believe the bias in favour of the developer must be ended – though that is not a recipe for ending development. No party could be more sensitive to public demand for better hospitals, schools and recreation facilities. We have to reconstruct our inner cities and protect our green spaces. We aim to reduce the demand for quarrying by reviewing the regulations and pursuing a public procurement policy which increases the use of secondary aggregates. We will seek stronger habitats protection and encourage a clean up initiative aimed at reducing derelict and contaminated land.

## Conclusion

New Labour's economic and environmental visions are interlinked. For too long we have been a nation of low wages, low standards, and low achievement. Labour's environmental commitment is part of our fundamental belief in the need to modernise Britain's economy and society.

Aiming for sustainability means counting the social and environmental costs as well as the economic impact of decisions. It means recognising the global dimension of environmental degradation and the acute responsibilities of the industrialised world in that context.

The engineering profession should rightly have expectations of a Labour government, in education, training, research and development, and sector consultations and partnerships on the way forward. But much will be expected in return. A Labour government will seek nothing less than the transformation of our society as we head towards the millennium. As we say in the opening words of *In Trust for Tomorrow*:

> "The air we breathe, the water we drink, the land we inhabit, the countryside we enjoy: these are fundamental issues that affect us all. At heart, the fate of the environment is about the wellbeing of people."

The engineering profession is uniquely placed to contribute to the goal of environmentally sustainable development – I trust you will want to join with us in that quest.

## References

1 *This Common Inheritance: UK Annual Report 1995*, Cm 2822, HMSO, 1995

2 *Greening the Treaty: A Manifesto for the Inter Governmental Conference from UK members of the European Environment Bureau*, c/o Council for the Protection of Rural England, 1995

3 *Our Common Future* (The Brundtland Report), Report of the 1987 World Commission on Environment and Development, Oxford University Press, 1987

4 *Science and Technology in Schools*, Report of the Commons Education Committee, HMSO, 1995

5 *Realising our Potential: A Strategy for Science, Engineering and Technology*, Office of Science and Technology, Cabinet Office, Cm 2250, HMSO, 1993

6 *ET 95: Second Annual Report on the British Environmental Technology Industry Survey*, Environmental Policy Consultants, 1995

## Questions to Joan Ruddock

**David Barrow** University of Cardiff

There is a lot of chattering in European political circles about the imposition of a carbon tax. This seems to me to be an end of pipe solution to our environmental problems. Do you have a view on this and would Labour implement a carbon tax if it were recommended by the European Parliament?

### Joan Ruddock

We do have a view. The problem with a carbon tax is this. If it is imposed equally, then those who are the poorest in society are going to pay the same tax at the same rate. They often, for example, have housing with poor insulation and need to use more. So there is that inequality and that inequity is one of the problems with the fiscal implements. If there were to be a carbon tax introduced compulsorily, then it would be absolutely vital to deal with the social equity problem. That would mean, for example, a thorough going programme of insulation. The Government would have to take responsibility for that. We would expect to be able to do it, for example, in a self financing package with the fuel industries and so we think it could be done if we had to do it. We agree with you, it's an end of pipe solution. We shouldn't always just say the polluter pays for pollution, or indeed that the conservator should pay. We should aim to reduce the problem from the start of the process rather than the end of the process. That is why we say that initially there are huge savings to be made in other forms of energy conservation. Industry already knows that. Many industries have dramatically reduced their energy consumption. So it is one instrument, probably not the best. I have just come back from Strasbourg, as it happens, and my discussions with people there are that the Commission has a revised proposal, which, if a carbon tax is introduced, it could be at a zero VAT rating. There will be choice. We think there are many other instruments and as I hope I have clearly indicated, if we are to have a carbon tax we must deal with the social equity problem.

### Professor Meredith Thring FEng

The question I want to ask is what would the Labour party do about the fundamental problem that the fuel supplying industry and the electricity industry want to sell more and this is contrary, of course, to the public interest?

### Joan Ruddock

You won't be surprised to know that I agree with you entirely and this is one of the reasons that we were totally opposed to the privatisation of the utilities. We don't believe that it is in the national interest to hand over utilities to private profit making. The fact is it has happened, it's there. So we have to use regulation and regulation is what we will use. We have made it very clear that we intend to use the regulator and a new framework of regulation so that there will be very clear targets set. We would expect to be able to follow the example of other nations, particularly Germany and Japan, where they are able to reduce consumption and at the same time have economic growth. We are determined to achieve that. It is completely unacceptable that people should be encouraged to squander a very precious resource in order that others can make private profits.

**Nick Cooke** British Nuclear Fuels plc

You said just now that the bias in favour of the developer must be ended. Would you not recognise that, whilst developers, in transport, energy, industrial, and housing fields obviously have a big say in the planning process, there are also environmental pressure groups, Nimbys, who have an equal say, an equally vocal say. In some senses, both groups are a minority in society. How would you address the question of how the consumer's interest in society is recognised, both the consumer of what is being developed and the consumer of the environment? Has Labour got plans to bring that much broader group in society into the development decision making without lengthening the planning process?

## Joan Ruddock

You are right to suggest that this is a great challenge. We are currently involving a panel of experts to give advice and to discuss with them how we might revise the planning process to be more democratic. We don't want it to be longer. Certainly in many cases it should be shorter. I want to take you up on your basic premise. When we speak about the bias in favour of the developer it is quite simply because there have been many cases, and out of town shopping centres are perhaps one of the easiest accessible examples, where the local population, is importantly affected. I don't regard that as a Nimby situation. We have had that kind of development, driven by developers. A lot of people, local and in government, realised that this was a bad strategy. It had enormous pollution problems e.g. of car use, decline of the local economy, death of the high street, all that. Yet where the local planning process would have actually said no the government said yes to the developer. It is that situation that has given developers a bad name. As I have made quite clear, we are in favour of development, it needs to be sustainable and we need a much better democratic input. The interests of the consumer are not always identical with the interests of those who would produce the product and so we have to get that balance. Whereas pressure groups can be a great irritation, especially I know, to British Nuclear Fuels, they often, though not in extreme cases, represent a strand of public opinion that cannot be organised in any other way. Very frequently, if you look at the membership of the conservation groups in Britain, which now has a membership of about 5 million, it does indicate I think that they are well bedded into the population and many of the issues they raise on questions of pollution are ones for which they have very broad public sympathy. I think it is quite instructive that it won't just be a Labour government that has to take account of that public opinion, it's very clear that the present Government has also begun to take account of it

## Professor Roland Clift OBE FEng University of Surrey

Putting the words 'energy' and 'policy' together in the same sentence is music to the ears. I would be interested to know where the Labour party sees the nuclear generating sector in that energy policy?

## Joan Ruddock

I shall not give a long historical perspective. Just to say quite simply that nuclear power is part of the present provision of energy generation. It will continue under a Labour government. We've said two very clear things. One, that we would not allow nuclear power stations to run beyond the point at which they can run safely. We want much more openness, there has been a recent example of the nuclear industry behaving badly. We want to ensure that never happens again. We will not agree to the construction of new nuclear power stations in this country.

# The Challenges for Enterprise

**Sir Robin Ibbs KBE**

Chairman

Lloyds Bank plc

## Personal Profile

**Sir Robin Ibbs** became a Deputy Chairman of Lloyds Bank plc in October 1988 and senior Deputy Chairman in January 1989. He also became Chairman of Lloyds Merchant Bank Holdings Ltd and Deputy Chairman of Lloyds Bank Canada in January 1989. He has been a Director of the Bank since April 1985. He succeeded Sir Jeremy Morse as Chairman in February 1993.

Sir Robin spent much of his career with ICI plc, which he joined in 1952 and from which he retired in April 1988. From 1972-76 he was a Director of Imperial Metal Industries Ltd. (now IMI plc). He joined the Board of ICI as an Executive Director in 1976. From 1980-82 he was seconded to the Cabinet Office as Head of the Central Policy Review Staff (the "Think Tank"). He returned to ICI as an Executive Director in 1982. From 1983-88 he was the Prime Minister's Adviser on Efficiency & Effectiveness in Government, a part-time appointment and in 1987 developed the civil service reform now know as *Next Steps*. He was a Member of the Top Salaries Review Body from 1983-89. In 1990 he led the Review of House of Commons Services. He was Knighted in 1982 and became a KBE in 1988. He received the British Institute of Management's Special Award in 1989. He became an Honorary Fellow of University College London in February 1993.

From 1976-80 he was a Member of the Governing Body and the Council of the British National Committee of the International Chamber of Commerce and Chairman of its Finance and General Purposes Committee. From 1978-80 he was a Member of the Industrial Development Advisory Board, Department of Industry. From 1976-79 and 1982-87 he was a member of the Council of the Chemical Industries Association and from 1983-87 a Vice-President. He is now an Honorary Member of the Association. From 1982-87 he was a Member of the Council of the Confederation of British Industry. From 1983-88 he was a member of the Court of the Cranfield Institute of Technology. He was a Member of the Council of the Royal Institute of International Affairs form 1983-89. Since 1988 he has been Deputy Chairman of the Isaac Newton Trust. In 1989 he became Chairman of the Council of University College London. He became a Fellow and Vice-President of the Chartered Institute of Bankers in 1993 and President of the Bankers' Club in 1994.

Sir Robin was educated at Greshams School; Upper Canada College; Toronto University; and Trinity College, Cambridge where he read mechanical sciences. He was later called to the Bar and is a member of Lincoln's Inn. He received the Honorary Degree of Doctor of Science from Bradford University in 1986 and the Honorary Degree of Doctor of Laws from Bath University in 1993.

# The Challenges for Enterprise

## Sir Robin Ibbs KBE

This morning's session of the Conference is headed *The Expectations of Society* and I am down on the programme to speak to you about *The Challenges for Enterprise*. Let me explain how I see this fitting together. I should emphasise that I use the word 'enterprise' in the sense of willingness to undertake new things.

The whole subject of Sustainable Development arises because society, in this as in so many other contexts, wants to have its cake and eat it. Across the world, society wants economic growth, and continued improvement in living standards in the widest sense. At the same time it wants this to be achieved without significant damage to the environment, and without destroying precious resources.

At first sight the expectations may appear unreasonable; at best there appears to be a difficult battle between material progress and an uneasy conscience. To take just an example: the public wants new roads to be built to overcome traffic congestion and to improve economic efficiency, but it also wants our countryside and our ancient sites to be preserved. The media often seem to delight in such dilemmas. Governments are urged to increase economic growth; advertisers urge consumers to spend, sometimes it seems almost regardless of environmental consequences. At the same time there are horror stories about environmental damage with dire consequences for future generations.

There is, of course, no easy answer. But the situation is not hopeless. Without question some traditional ways of doing things have to be moderated or completely changed; but often this stimulates the development of new acceptable ways of achieving the same ends. In some cases, the implications of the perceived problem are very widespread, in others relatively narrow. Each instance has to be considered separately. In many, science and ingenuity can provide a way through. This is where enterprise comes in. The enterprise of engineers in devising acceptable practical solutions that deliver what science offers; and the enterprise of people with money in taking a risk and financially backing these solutions. It is the marriage of creative technical enterprise with well judged financial enterprise that provides the way forward to growth in acceptable sustainable ways.

As society becomes increasingly aware of dangers to the environment, tighter regulation by governments and increasing social pressures will rightly rule out some obvious opportunities for economic growth. But ingenuity can often provide new ways of moving forward. The *Clean Air Act* by forbidding dirty inefficient open fires has contributed substantially to much improved domestic heating in this country; likewise concern about $CO_2$ is now resulting in more efficient use of energy. Through better technology based on scientific advances, environmental improvement and economic progress can go hand in hand.

Of course there is nothing new in this. It may be only in recent years that the media have become acutely aware of the environment, but engineers have been concerned with protecting it for years. The need for clean water and the safe disposal of sewage was widely appreciated well back in the last century.

Engineers were able to provide water supplies, sewers and sewage disposal plants because money was forthcoming to fund their schemes. Again, engineers have been providing, for almost as long, plants in the chemical and other process industries which have had, quite rightly, to meet steadily rising standards of effluent control. Science and good engineering have produced equipment for which funding has been found because the projects, as well as meeting higher standards, offered satisfactory financial returns or enabled an adequate return to continue.

There is no better example of what can be achieved by enterprise than the story of new substances to replace CFCs. When it became clear that, because of the risk of damage to the ozone layer, CFCs were no longer acceptable, new science and creative engineering produced alternatives and new production plants in a remarkably short time. The team concerned has rightly won awards. Their technical enterprise was backed by correspondingly enterprising investment. But nothing stands still, and there are always opportunities for further improvements.

The replacement of CFCs demonstrates that one important challenge is to keep abreast of scientific advances and to encourage scientific research in areas where progress could provide a major breakthrough.

CFCs are a notable example where the need for Sustainable Development has brought about a major change. But there are many more examples of new ideas and new products that have been stimulated, ranging from high temperature cracking of waste material to electronic equipment for recording road use as a basis for charging.

In truth, the challenge of new perceptions, and a need to solve new problems, has the merit of breaking the mould of established practices. It creates exceptional opportunities for vigorous enterprise.

But we must be unflinchingly realistic. As knowledge and awareness of environmental and similar problems increases, some extremely painful decisions can arise. Some manufacturing processes will have to cease entirely; in other instances, the unavoidable corrective action may clearly be uneconomic. The cost of a limited number of extreme cases of this kind will have to be accepted, but the bulk of business and social activity has got to remain economically sound – it is not possible to put the normal rules of economics into abeyance for the sake of the environment. In the long run if you don't make a profit you cannot make anything. Even the government cannot solve problems by using tax income unless there is a thriving economy from which the taxes can be raised. Society cannot choose poverty as a way through these problems. That is why creative enterprise (and I am referring to creative enterprise which produces good returns) is essential for achieving Sustainable Development.

The great challenge for enterprise is therefore the one it always faces, to find out what consumers need, to find out the constraints within which progress must be found, but then to create answers which will yield a respectable economic return.

Nevertheless, I must emphasise that enterprise involves taking risks. Some schemes, some projects, some inventions don't work out in practice. This may be for technical reasons, or commercial reasons, or both. Good judgement is at the heart of successful enterprise, but you have to recognise that you cannot win them all. This is something of which bankers are extremely aware.

It is the business of bankers to lend money and their professional skill lies in assessing risk. The greatly increased concern about the environment in recent years has widened the aspects of risk that they have to consider. Not only do they have to assess the financial merits of a business or a project, but they now also have to assess its possible impact on the environment. Lloyds Bank has produced a comprehensive environmental risk guide for its lenders. This runs to 250 pages of detailed information. It ranges, for example, from the *European Agreement on the International Carriage of Dangerous Goods by Road*, to the specific risks arising from etching and electroplating in the manufacture of electronic equipment. Awareness of environmental risk may cause bankers to refuse to lend. But greater understanding of these issues can also persuade them to support an invention that offers an acceptable way through.

Even so, vigorous enterprise requires wider financial support than bankers alone can be expected to provide. Contrary to popular belief, banks do not really have money of their own; they only have depositors' money and (a much smaller amount) shareholders' money.

Because of their duty to look after depositors and shareholders, although banks are not risk averse, there is a limit to the scale of risk they can face. Enterprise needs injections of committed risk capital known as equity, in addition to loans and overdrafts. Large and medium sized companies, with confidence in their development projects, can usually provide or raise these funds. However, small businesses, including start-ups, play a crucial role as seed beds for new ideas and enterprise; they can have great difficulty in attracting equity finance. Venture capital funds, and rich individuals willing to take a risk with part of their wealth, so-called business angels, are possible sources. In this country we need more people of this kind, which is a further reason why a strong prosperous economy is so important if enterprise is to enable us to drive forward in new acceptable ways.

Technical resources and financial resources are not infinite. Both should be found at the places where they are most needed, where a breakthrough would make a great difference. In practice, the effectiveness of pressure groups and people who are deeply concerned can influence what gets attention. It is important that particular issues should not be exaggerated and that balanced judgement should determine priorities. I can think of examples where unnecessarily stringent regulation has led to a major diversion of technical and financial resources. In the extreme, exaggerated and poorly informed concern can lead to bad decisions on particular issues; many would argue this was true with Brent Spar. I can think of examples where excessive fear has led to complete stagnation on an important issue. Such deadlock is a major threat to Sustainable Development. Unwarranted scare stories can do immense damage.

One challenge for enterprise, therefore, is to focus on the genuinely important problem and not to be distracted by the hubbub of exaggeration. Sorting out such situations can be very difficult and much of it is a task for government and regulators. But it is the responsibility of enterprise to help where it is both needed and has something to bring, and to make sure that there is awareness of what applied science and ingenuity may be able to offer in a given situation. It is here that a sense of balance is so important, something engineers are very familiar with. In their work they are used to having to balance many factors in making a decision, whether this relates to a large project or the design of a small part. It is a crucial aspect of their professional skill and should contribute significantly in the search for opportunities for sustainable development.

I believe that in nearly all difficult situations, openness and good communication are the best safeguards; fear builds up when people think unpleasant truth is being suppressed. One of the key challenges for enterprise is to ensure that as engineers and financial backers open up opportunities for Sustainable Development, good communication ensures that the merits of what is proposed are widely known and that unjustified fears are put at rest.

These are exciting times and there are exciting opportunities. I have drawn attention to some of the ways in which engineering enterprise and financial enterprise can contribute to Sustainable Development; indeed such enterprise is essential to achieving it. Furthermore, the search for Sustainable Development can prove to be both good for the environment and good for business. I have also spelled out one or two challenges that have to be faced.

Obviously, what I have been saying is very general and many of the points are relevant beyond the UK. But our own history has seen periods of outstanding enterprise – merchant traders in the Middle Ages, inventors and entrepreneurs in the Industrial Revolution, the national energy that built the British Empire. In recent years there has been some evidence of a fresh resurgence in enterprise. Also we continue to be a highly innovative country in science. The need for Sustainable Development could prove to be a great opportunity for this country to make a notable contribution, not only to its own prosperity, but also to the well being of the world community, through imaginative new applications of science. This is truly a great challenge for UK enterprise.

But this is an engineering occasion and I want to end by emphasising the role of engineers in all this. One of the reasons for Sustainable Development being so important a subject is that we are in an era of rapid change – new science, new technology, new expectations of society. Engineers of every discipline are people who put ideas into practice, who combine scientific advances with hard experience and deliver new benefits for society. Because of the current rapidity of change there are going to be enormous calls on engineers and their skills. As in the great days of Brunel, Telford, Stephenson and many others, society will increasingly recognise their importance. The need for Sustainable Development is not only a wonderful challenge for enterprise; it is also an exciting and richly rewarding prospect for engineers.

## Questions to Sir Robin Ibbs

**Joanna Howard** Roffey Park Management Institute

I very much enjoyed your talk, it was very clarifying. It has left me with two questions. Given the environmental effect of short term, profit driven thinking that we have seen in the last, say, ten years, I'm wondering if two things ought to be thought about. A re-evaluation of what we mean by profit, perhaps with a slightly longer term focus on it, and perhaps a naive wish that bankers and engineers could be in the forefront of this kind of thinking rather than being dragged by regulation and public outcry into taking the enterprises and innovation that we have seen.

**Sir Robin Ibbs**

Well those I find very penetrating and quite difficult questions. To redefine what one means by profit and how one measures profit is a sort of far distant goal which people keep returning to from time to time. And it carries with it what I would call in very simple terms dangers of having multiple objectives. As soon as you give managers multiple objectives you are to some extent giving them decisions of choice which then get in the way of their doing the real managing you are asking them to do. For that reason I do believe that there is a very heavy responsibility on society, and on politicians in particular, to set sensible frameworks in which the main hazards that you are referring to, where short term profit may take you down the wrong road, are dealt with by the regulatory framework and the people who are running businesses can get on with the job with fairly simple targets. Now, so far as engineers and bankers being involved in such processes, I think that one gets involved to the extent that one deserves to be and of course it's nice if those taking decisions come along and ask us. But in this area there is a heavy duty upon major groups in society, when they have something to say, to think about it extremely carefully before they say it.

**Professor Roger Wootten FEng** City University

I would like to ask what responsibilities you think bankers have in the case of an engineering project that is proposed to you for finance which is of low risk but not sustainable in environmental terms?

**Sir Robin Ibbs**

We provide very detailed guidance for our lenders. A small project which was considered locally would be turned down as a result of that guidance. But there are of course big projects and however careful you were in drawing up that sort of guidance there are grey areas where something sits on the edge and difficult decisions are needed. And I can assure you that in those cases those decisions come right up the line. One has to consider at the top whether something is or is not acceptable. If it is not acceptable then we would not back it.

**Donald Bruce** Church of Scotland

You mentioned exaggeration being one of the problems with regard to the environmental consequences etc. The problems which I observe from where I sit in Edinburgh is that the public often feel that they don't have any say in a lot of the regulatory decisions that are made, and are therefore prey to exaggeration from all quarters because they themselves haven't got the access to the people who could say, on the one hand 'Yes here is a technical problem which engineers are facing and there are the environmental problems etc'. And I wonder if you have any thoughts as to how you can better involve the public to enable this balance you refer to, to be found?

## Sir Robin Ibbs

The point that I was making is that communication is of the essence for solving that sort of problem. How one is going to do that communicating becomes the key question and to really look into that today is, I think, difficult. But there is a great duty on what I would call the focal points of communication, that is the press and the media, television and radio. They, to some extent, have to provide the opportunity for people who have good knowledge of the subject and are capable of spelling out in simple terms, to be given a say at the right moment. Now part of the problem, and we are coming back very close to the question about profit, is that these organisations, even if they are not driven by profit, are all driven by numbers of viewers and listeners and copies of newspapers sold. An exaggerated story makes a much better basis for selling a lot of newspapers than the calm, analytical views of some very well informed person who writes an article for it in the centre pages. I am afraid that this is where society has got to put some sort of reform pressure sooner or later on the media, whether it's on invasion of privacy which a lot of people feel extremely strongly about, or whether it's on failure to give balanced reports on subjects which are prone to exaggerated comment. I am afraid that I am not in a position this morning to enter into a dissertation on what we might do about the media because I am a great believer in freedom of the press so I'm well and truly caught in the centre!

## Sir Frank Gibb CBE FEng Chairman of the Energy Saving Trust

We of course are trying to encourage people and small enterprises to improve energy efficiency, this I call a stick regulation. We need something of a carrot as well in order to start a trend towards using a new appliance or a new form of car or something like this and I wonder how you feel about a sort of pump priming approach where funds are made available in order to start that trend. Not to carry on year after year but just to start an initiative so that manufacturers get encouraged and the public sees what's happening?

## Sir Robin Ibbs

There are cases where that sort of approach is undoubtedly necessary and they occur in commerce normally, as well as in the situations that you describe. In fact, to make it international for a moment, the Japanese are positively famous for it. If they want to introduce an important new product into a completely different part of the world, they will decide where they want to be in due course. They will, in effect, make a capital investment at the beginning, by being prepared to operate at a loss until they achieve the turnover which is necessary for the thing to make a return. Where we have objectives which are susceptible to that approach it is necessary to make what I would describe as a capital investment. As in all cases of capital investment it's the quality of the project i.e. is it going to work or not by putting in this first injection of money? Shall we ever get a return on our investment? Shall we get the change of habit that we want? This is just a matter of severely judging the project. If it passes the test of such a judgement then of course it is right to do some pump priming and put some money upfront.

# Consumers: The Neglected Dimension of Sustainable Development

**Dame Rachel Waterhouse**

Former Chairman
Consumers' Association

## Personal Profile

**Dame Rachel Waterhouse** was educated at King Edward's High School, St Hugh's College Oxford and the University of Birmingham. She has been involved in consumer activities for over 30 years.

She was Chairman of the Consumers' Association between 1982-90 having served on the Council since 1966.

She served as a member of the National Consumer Council between 1975-86 and the Consumers' Consultative Committee of the EEC Commission between 1977-84. She has also served on the Price Commission, the Council of the Advertising Standards Authority and the NEDC and as a member of the Health and Safety Commission.

In 1980 Dame Rachel was appointed President of the Institute of Consumer Ergonomics, University of Loughborough having served as Chairman for the previous decade. She is also Vice President of the National Federation of Consumer Groups.

# Consumers:
# The Neglected Dimension of Sustainable Development
## Dame Rachel Waterhouse

Sustainable Development can mean pretty much what the speaker wants it to mean. Environmentalists tend to stress 'sustainable' while others, particularly Governments in underdeveloped countries, understandably focus on 'development'. Depending on one's point of view other variations in the terminology may be used, such as Sustainable Growth or Sustainable Consumption. I'm talking today about the perspective of consumers, whose agreement, help and co-operation are essential to the achievement of a more sustainable use of environmental resources – and who, ultimately, will benefit most in this and in future generations.

The consumer objective must be to define the level and type of consumption that is compatible with a sustainable environment that is also safe and pleasant. From this arises the key question: does Sustainable Consumption imply consuming less or just consuming differently? To seek answers to this question, a major conference was held in Holland two years ago by the then International Organisation of Consumer Unions, now Consumers' International – the worldwide body that brings together over 200 consumer organisations from some 70 countries.

Consumer representatives from developed and developing areas of the world looked at current consumption patterns and indications of environmental damage. They agreed that it was essential for the global consumer movement to pick up the challenges thrown down by the Rio Summit, and to seek some statement that could be accepted by the 'haves' and 'have-nots' of the five continents.

Such agreement was not easy to achieve, but the conference – which has been highly influential in the development of consumer organisations' thinking and policy – did take the major step of agreeing this definition of Sustainable Consumption: "*A level of consumption that meets the present and future needs and aspirations of people the world over, from all sectors of society, without compromising the sustainability of the environment and its life support systems.*"

Such a general definition of principle is only the beginning of a process that will see many arguments along the way, but it lays a clear emphasis on the needs and aspirations of consumers worldwide. It acknowledges the reality that every human society has always interacted with the environment, has always used resources and left its mark on the world for good or ill. That, of course, in one sense, is what we mean by engineering.

This definition also rejects the view, that some environmentalists have put forward, of the environment as a sacrosanct entity that must be preserved intact for its own sake, and that sustainability is simply a matter of dividing up known resources between members of the existing population. The world's physical resources are, in a sense, finite – but our assessments of them, and our ingenuity in using them, are constantly developing. Consumers worldwide have real and pressing needs, some of which can only be met in ways which influence the environment whether through the consumption of natural resources, or the development of open land, or the construction of major civil engineering projects. I am talking here about meeting basic needs such as clean water, sanitary housing conditions, safe transport systems and adequate food supplies as well as expansion of consumer choice in the already diverse markets of rich western countries. Some messages from consumer representatives – particularly in developing countries – may be uncomfortable for many environmentalists, but they are realistic and must be accepted and met.

However, consumer demands are not fixed or incapable of change in the wider public interest. Just as we castigate the profligacy of the past, future generations' aspirations may be (indeed probably will be) different from those of today. We must be reasonably flexible in interpreting likely consumer demands on the environment – there is certainly no case for simply rolling forward present patterns of consumption and expenditure and multiplying them by the size of the population or the volume of our Gross Domestic Product. What is required is to acknowledge the legitimate claim of future generations on the present, to take a view of the environment over time, and fully to understand that the squandering of resources today places in serious jeopardy the outlook for future generations.

The crucial question then is *how* we are to meet *growing* needs and aspirations using the *available* resources. It will require careful and cautious use of resources and energy, innovation and ingenuity in the design and manufacture of goods, and care in the planning and implementation of services. It has a powerful message for consumers and producers alike.

Where does the responsibility for sustainability lie? With consumers or producers? Green campaigners like the environmental group *Sustainability* have urged consumers to switch voluntarily to a more sustainable lifestyle and give up things they don't need. Top of their list of things we could all do without are air conditioning and bottled water. They suggest a shift from the eighties 'global consumer' concerned only with me, materialism, greed and short term gain to the nineties 'world citizen' whose watch words are we, enough, quality of life and long term responsibilities.

Many of us may feel that we would be waiting a long time for consumers voluntarily to eschew some of the benefits of modern life. One central problem is that there are very few big environmental gains to be achieved through minor changes in people's lifestyles. The really important effects private consumers have on the environment are mostly in energy and transport use. But here we find the benefits consumers have worked hardest to gain. How many of us are prepared to give up our cars despite the mounting evidence of damage to the immediate local environment here in London, let alone the long term environmental damage globally? How many of us are prepared to forego well-heated houses, comfortable throughout the winter? It is clear that our own long term interest in a clean and healthy environment is in conflict with our short term interest in our own standard of living, with the comfort, convenience and freedom that car travel brings.

Political will and commercial interests may, however, make it easier and more attractive for people to behave in ways which are friendlier to the environment.

Already consumers have been easily persuaded to give up products which do not affect their life-style. They buy aerosols and refrigerators which do not contain HFCs and cheaper lead-free petrol, and they recycle bottles and waste-paper. Each of these appears to have a short term as well as a long term benefit in terms of either health, economy or convenience. Consumers want to preserve the environment, but they also want to avoid illness, to save money and not to be inundated and frustrated by mountains of waste packaging. Given the task of bringing these two aspects together, design engineers have already made great strides, but far more remains to be done.

Transparency and information are vital, if consumers are to play their part. They need to be aware that not every old refrigerator is safely dismantled; that lead-free petrol does nothing to save the ozone layer; and that some recycling in terms of energy and pollution may cost more than it saves.

Industry has other responsibilities. It will find itself under pressure to do more than just comply with environmental legislation. The message of Brent Spar is that manufacturing and operational procedures as well as end products and services will increasingly come under public scrutiny. Engineers will have to consider environmentally the whole process from the use of raw materials through to the disposal of waste products and out-of-date plant. This is as true for Brent Spar or the nuclear power station as it is for the domestic refrigerator or motor car. Only when this is clear can consumers make sensible sustainable choices.

For our part, we at Consumers' Association need no convincing of the vital part that engineers have to play in this process. We have used engineering skills and concepts in our own product testing and standardisation work ever since our foundation in 1957, and employ several teams of specialists at our new Product Research Centre in Milton Keynes, which opened in April this year. In recent years, we have taken an increasing interest in the civil engineering side, too, especially through our work on public utilities, and in testing water pumps for use in developing countries, on behalf of the World Bank. But whether the wider public is sufficiently aware of the contribution of engineering disciplines is much less certain.

This conference will help to get that message across. But it is clearly not going to be enough, and three basic requirements will have to be met.

First, the distinctive contribution of engineers needs to be 'sold' not just at gatherings like this one but within the organisation in which you work. I suspect that, if you asked informed consumers who has most to contribute to solving the problems of sustainability, many would mention environmental lobbyists, consumer organisations, and perhaps official regulators. And within industry, I suspect many would expect the lead for more sustainable products and services to come from marketing and advertising departments, coupled perhaps with those who design green logos to go on packaging. There is a clear need for engineers to take centre stage in showing how their skills can provide solutions which benefit everyone.

The second requirement is for organisations of all kinds to recognise that this is part of a long haul, which will require substantial commitments of time and energy in research, testing, evaluation and monitoring. Sustainability by definition, is a long-term goal requiring long-term solutions, as such it is the antithesis of the short-termism which still pervades too much of our national life. It is not easy to persuade boards of directors that the temptation to make short-term gains might need to be resisted, but that is a message which must be understood.

Third, and most important, technological development – however imaginative and inspired – will not get far off the drawing board unless it is in step with consumer needs, aspirations and concerns. Generation of electricity by wind power and electric cars may meet consumers' concerns, but currently scarcely their demands and aspirations. As I have already stressed, these are not immutable and can change rapidly over time, but it is absolutely pointless designing solutions to the problems people haven't got, still less introducing new approaches which consumers don't understand, or mistrust.

This in turn, requires a commitment to transparency and a willingness to explain and reassure.

There is also much to be gained from effective communication and dialogue, both directly with consumers and with representatives of consumer organisations, whose perceptions are already changing.

Consumers' Association, with which I have long been associated, exerts a powerful influence on behalf of consumers nationally and particularly on behalf of their members and magazine subscribers. At CA we have traditionally defended and lobbied on behalf of consumers *today*. We have worked very hard both within our magazines and our campaigns to achieve our mission statement of *"empowering consumers to make informed decisions'* and *'achieving measurable improvements in goods and services".* Time and again we have restated the key principles of consumer rights to access, choice, information, safety, redress and the right to be heard.

In defending rights of current consumers there has sometimes been a temptation to put to one side the long term interest of future consumers. But our mission makes no such distinction, and increasingly at CA we are undertaking work that takes on board this broader understanding of the consumer interest in the long term. The environment is among the many issues of vital concern to consumers over their whole lifetime, and beyond.

Engineering for Sustainable Development

One remit we have already taken up is that of scrutinising environmental claims whether they come from Government, industry or green campaigners. The need for better information on environmental subjects is vast. Environmental problems can be difficult for consumers to grasp. The best environmental options can be unclear or the result of a difficult balancing act between competing claims. Even the simplest problems (such as advice to consumers on whether terry or disposable nappies are more environmentally damaging) are in fact very difficult problems to solve. Proper technical analysis is always complex and must consider the burden on the environment over the whole lifecycle (say of a product or a building) and weigh up environmental concerns that are not easily quantifiable or comparable. There is a need for better information and for independent scrutiny, on behalf of consumers, of the often conflicting assessments of environmental impact. Each case must be considered on its merits. Incremental change, where the scientific consensus backs up the arguments, must be the way forward.

Consumer groups can act as a two-way channel of communication putting forward consumer views. Unlike many other public interest bodies, we have a very broad remit and are used to dealing with conflicting objectives, between say, choice on the one side and better environmental safety on the other. We are well aware that trade-offs need to be made. Consumer groups have much to offer to public debate on the right balance between environmental and consumer friendliness.

However, what consumers can do individually is limited by the infrastructure and technology of the modern world. Choices available to consumers are circumscribed by the engineered environment and engineers have a key role and responsibility to work alongside consumers to make sustainable choices. Creative engineering that searches for sustainable options and provides sustainable choice, is the real engineering challenge waiting to be taken up.

## Questions to Dame Rachel Waterhouse

### Member of Audience

Can I ask what your attitude is to marking on consumer goods the energy consumed in its manufacture and the energy consumed in its use?

### Dame Rachel Waterhouse

The problem we have always had with labelling is to get an effective label that will convey information fully and accurately. For example, developing a label about fat content of food takes a very long time. Our washing machine tests which just used to be 'will it wash' now actually tell you how much water it will use and how much electricity. So we are much more aware in those tests of energy consumption in the home by the person who is actually using the product.

### Jim Hopwood Exxon Chemical

Thank you very much indeed for asking what you describe as the key question which I think was 'Does sustainable consumption imply consuming less or just consuming differently?'. I think that is the key question and I am not sure what conclusion the Association reached. It seems to me that if we do some fairly simple arithmetic on rates of use of materials and rates of degradation of the environment, then numerate people must reach the conclusion that the present rates of use are not sustainable. Numerate people have therefore a very strong moral obligation to try to get that message across to society. The question is do you agree with that and, as an expert in consumer affairs, how can we get that message over successfully?

### Dame Rachel Waterhouse

I have been talking about the worldwide consumer. I find that at meetings like these that I go to, that we talk in very strong middle class terms. We all have a motor car, perhaps we all have central heating, some of us even have air conditioning. But if you take different sections of society then you can't ask everybody in society to consume less, so there isn't a straight answer to that. The answer basically is that if, for example, you take a washing machine, that was engineered to use less water, to use less energy and create soapsuds which do less damage to the environment, that information can be used by the consumer. The consumer can make the choice and that's what I meant by my last slide about engineers enabling consumers to make sustainable choices. Then they will be consuming differently and consuming less at the same time. Take transport. What are the options available, apart from the motor car or a declining public transport system? So I think that your question can't be answered by individual consumers; they have got to have the environment in which they can make choices about both consuming less and consuming differently. Engineers are vital to creating those choices. That really is the message that I wanted to get over today.

# The Ethical Input to Engineering Decisions

## The Rt Reverend Richard Harries DD FKC

Bishop of Oxford

## Personal Profile

**The Rt Reverend Richard Harries** has been Bishop of Oxford since 1987. Previously he was Dean of King's College London. He has written books on a range of issues, most recently *Art and the Beauty of God* and *The Real God*, both published by Mowbrays. And, forthcoming, *Question in Faith*, to be published by SPCK. He has taught and lectured on a number of ethical concerns, contributing to the public debate. He is probably best known as a broadcaster, particularly through the *Thought for the Day* slot on BBC Radio 4's Today Programme.

Before ordination, he was commissioned in the Royal Corps of Signals and originally had a place at Cambridge to read Mechanical Sciences, before switching to Theology. He contributed to the thinking of the report by the Churches Energy Group on *Energy*.

# The Ethical Input to Engineering Decisions

## The Rt Reverend Richard Harries DD FKC

## Introduction

Under the overall theme of "the expectations of society" I have been asked to speak on the ethical input to engineering decisions. The basic ethical imperatives coming from society, which underlie this whole Conference are three. First, protection of the environment, secondly, conservation of non-renewable resources and thirdly, the need, especially in the Third World, for continuing economic development. These moral imperatives are now widely shared in our society, have been accepted by all political parties and, as far as the first two are concerned, have significantly shaped legislation. This wide consensus does not depend on any one religious view. It is shared by people of all religions and none. They are moral convictions which seem to belong to our very humanity. Nevertheless, when each of us explores the rationale or basis for these convictions, we touch that borderline where ethics can tip over into something else. The poet Gerard Manley Hopkins wrote:

> What would the world be, once bereft
> Of wet and wilderness? Let them be left,
> O let them be left, wildness and wet:
> Long live the weeds and the wilderness yet.

But why should we leave the marshes and deserts? There is a limit to what we can provide in the way of utilitarian or economic arguments. When a million species have perished and a million remain why should we be concerned to preserve a particular insect or flower? In the end no purely utilitarian answer is adequate. We come up against the value of creation in itself, for itself, in all its variety and richness. The same questions can be asked about our concern for generations yet unborn, that they can enjoy nature as we do and have the use of some non-renewable resources. We have not only inherited the earth from our grandparents; we have borrowed it from our grandchildren. But why do we feel the claim of this not yet existent future? Again we will stub, not our toes but our mind and spirits against the sheer, precious fact of the earth's existence. Concern about the environment is fashionable but it is not I think a passing fashion; nor is it just a matter of the survival of the planet – for the question arises as to why we think it's important to survive. It reflects the deeply felt response to life in which nature is experienced as refreshing and life-giving.

Some will find it surprising to see the need for continuing economic development set down as a moral conviction. Indeed some would argue, on moral grounds, for the end to growth or limits to growth. But that can't be true for the Third or developing world, where literally billions of people are still living at or below starvation level and where economic development is essential to pull them out of misery. It needs to be growth without environmental damage and growth with appropriate technology but growth there needs to be. As for us in the West, the economic forces behind growth are so powerful, it is difficult to think of our society radically changing direction. But, more important than that, there is something about the human spirit which goes for growth. The question is, what kind of growth? Clearly the challenge to our society is for growth that does not damage the environment or use up non-renewable resources. But there are many examples of this, the development of CDs for example and the whole microchip world. So we are looking for sustainable development, which the Brundtland Report defined as one which "meets the needs of the present generation without compromising the ability of future generations to meet their needs". Others prefer to talk of "ecologically sustainable development".

In the Institution of Civil Engineers *Rules for Professional Conduct* the first rule says:

> "A member in his responsibility to his employer and to the profession shall have
> full regard to the public interest, particularly in matters of health and safety."

The public interest is that in which we all have a stake, as opposed to sectional interest when only a few do. We all have an interest in clean air and good waste disposal systems. It has long been accepted that, as that rule says, a crucial aspect of the public interest in engineering projects, is health and safety. What has happened more recently is that concerns about the environment and the kind of world that our grandchildren will live in, have come to be seen by the public as just as much in everyone's interest as traditional concerns about health and safety.

Indeed, they are crucial aspects of health and safety. As engineers made such incredible contributions to health and safety in the 19th century, through ensuring supplies of clean water and proper sewage systems, which has done more for human health than almost any other advance, so today the public looks to engineers, working with others, to make a similar contribution in relation to current concerns.

Regard for the public interest is fundamental to all codes of conduct for the engineering profession. The question therefore is how engineers exercise their particular, professional responsibility for that public interest, particularly in relation to Sustainable Development. In this large and complex field I want to focus the discussion under three aspects, *The Precautionary Principle*, *Innovation* and *Ethics and Economics*.

## The Precautionary Principle

The first specific responsibility of engineers in relation to the public interest on this issue is to be alert from the beginning of a project to any possible risk to the environment and, we could add, the excessive use of non-renewable resources. This is as fundamental as a concern about traditional aspects of health and safety, which have long entered the very being of engineers. Environmental factors are becoming and need to become second nature.

The precautionary principle closely allied as it is to the preventative principle, is that society should not wait until environmental damage has occurred or the risk of damage is proven and measured before taking corrective action. As the Rio Declaration formulates it:

> "Where there are threats of serious or irreversible damage, lack of full scientific
> certainty should not be used as a reason for postponing cost effective measures
> to prevent environmental degradation".

This is in fact a very moderate expression of the principle with its emphasis on serious threats and the qualification about cost effective measures. Others would formulate the principle to take into account all damage to the environment or would not put any cost limits on taking the preventative measures necessary. However we formulate it, it must above all be the responsibility of the engineer to access the impact of a particular scheme on the environment and who must assess the risks involved before attempting construction. It is therefore a particular professional obligation on engineers to be rigorously scientific in the collection and assessment of data. There is then the further task of communicating this to all those involved in a project and this, today, includes the wider public. The need for a rigorously scientific, sober assessment and presentation of the facts is particularly important today with the advent of militant pressure groups of various kinds and the ease with which public opinion is swung by the media.

Yet here we come up against a dilemma. Is any gathering and presentation of the facts strictly neutral? Are there not assumptions and presuppositions behind all we do? So we find when a particular project is in dispute, scientists can be brought in on either side to supply evidence supporting different positions. I would have to say that there is nothing inherently wrong about this. The English adversarial system, in Parliament, in the courts as well as in public enquiries ensures that every view has a chance of being aired, nothing is suppressed, even if it means that it is much harder to reach a conclusion. But as nothing in this life is entirely neutral, there are assumptions and presuppositions in everything, the important thing is to be aware so far as we can what our own are. The public interest today suggests that there should be an underlying bias in favour of environmental protection, as there is an underlying bias in favour of safety. This does not override the prime obligation of scientific rigour, which is always desperately needed. But given that the selection and presentation of facts is never neutral, an instinctive reflex, a built-in bias towards the environment is what the public interest entails. It is crucial that this bias is there in managers and politicians for they decide what to do with the facts: but the presentation of the facts begins with engineers.

Communication is a key aspect of the engineer's role today. Communicating the facts of environmental impact to clients and educating the public as a whole. In particular they can play a key part in helping the public and politicians think in terms of life cycles rather than commodities. Most of us when we drink a can of coca-cola do not give a thought to where the materials came from or where and how they will be disposed. We are concerned with the immediate sensation. Engineers should be aware of the whole cycle and, together with others, of the true cost of that cycle including preventing environmental damage in the obtaining of the materials in the first place and recycling or disposing of the waste at the end. An awareness of the life-cycle can lead people to look for "closed loop systems" in the use of energy and materials, to the practice of good industrial ecology.

## Innovation

A word that recurs time and again in the literature on the subject of sustainable development is innovation, the need for innovative solutions. For example Chris Hampson of ICI said to the seminar on *Signposting the Sustainable Development Strategy* last year:

> "The first reaction of any technical company faced with an environmental issue may often be an attempt to solve it by the application of hardware and capital. Often these are end of pipe solutions. But the answer may lie in something more simple; the recycling of a by-product stream, an improvement in process efficiency, the re-design of a process. It is engineers and scientists who contributed to our problems by continuing to use processes and products that fit another era. It is now the job of these engineers and scientists to help us find innovative solutions."

He went on to say that he remained concerned that some issues are not being tackled with sufficient imagination and that we also need "innovation on finding new products and services to meet environmental requirements".

The justification for our hope in this area is that we human beings are by nature innovative, ingenuous, creative beings. It is, from a religious point of view, part of what is meant by being made *Imago Dei*. This has been proved time and again in history from the invention of the wheel through to the extraordinary advances that have taken place over the last 200 years. We are capable of looking at old problems in new ways and coming up with different, sometimes lateral ways of solving them.

But the will needs to be there. It is a well-known fact that in war the decisive factor is the will to win or resist. At the beginning of the Second World War the French army was in fact as large and well armed as the Germans. But at that stage the will to resist was not as strong as the will of the other side to dominate. There is no less of a war on to preserve our environment and conserve its variety of riches and resources for future generations. The will is needed not to rest content with yesterday's technology but to pursue doggedly and imaginatively fresh solutions to each problem. As human beings we have the innovative capacity, the ingenuity, the creativity to do this, if the will is there. A good example in recent years is the way that the sudden rise in oil prices in the 1970s and the 1980s led to a dramatic interest in saving fuel of all kinds and the technology to do this. The recent report from the House of Lords Select Committee on Sustainable Development argues that "we need appropriate fiscal and legal signposts to overcome barriers to the adoption of more sustainable lifestyles and patterns of consumption". This is probably true. But even before all those fiscal and legal incentives are in place, the determined will to find innovative solutions can be present in the engineer. The will is often there. But the money isn't. Or that's what we feel. Which leads me to my third focus.

## Ethics and Economics

People often perceive a clash between economic considerations, the need to make a profit and the claims of the environment. More enlightened businesses now reject that polarisation. It pays to take environmental factors seriously, first because of the need to conform to the increasing amount of legislation in this area, secondly because green is fashionable. When products are associated with an environmentally friendly company, this is a selling point. Thirdly, because concerns about the environment have given rise to the need for a whole new series of technologies and goods. There is new business here. None of this should surprise the ethicist. For it is fundamental to the Hebrew Scriptures, which are basic for Judaism and Christianity and, as modified by the Koran, to Islam – that to do what is right does in the end bring benefits. For the universe has a moral foundation. To do the right thing, in this case to take environmental claims and future generations fully into account, is to go with the grain of things and this in due course will bring its own proper reward. Environmental products are already worth 200 billion dollars a year world-wide and the environmental industry is expected to grow at a rate of 5.5% a year.

Nevertheless, on particular projects and in the short term, there is of course a proper tension between cost factors and environmental claims. To resolve this the Inspector of Pollution puts forward the criterion of BATNEEC – the best available techniques not entailing excessive cost.

Not entailing excessive cost. That sounds sensible enough: and it is sensible. What I mean is this. There is always a tendency in human life to make one claim absolute. In commercial life it always used to be the case that profit should override every other consideration. This has now given way, I am glad to say, in enlightened business, to the shareholder concept, with a number of claims being balanced one against another. On the other hand there are some environmentalists who urge that environmental considerations should always, in every case, override every other claim. The fact is, however, that in this finite, mortal life of ours no one claim can always have absolute status. As you know so well, every decision is a matter of balancing a whole range of factors. This cannot be avoided and is nothing to be ashamed of.

It is the very stuff of human decision-making so although the qualification, not entailing excessive cost sounds unexciting enough, it is a quite proper consideration and it goes along with the thrust of the first half of the criterion, the best available technology. The imperative to search for or develop that best available technology is firmly in place.

Here again I see engineers playing a key role. For between the pressures of the market on the one hand and those from environmental pressure groups on the other, the engineer is the person who knows what the best available technology is at any one point and who is familiar with its cost implications. Engineers will have a key role to play in where the balance is finally struck. One of the problems of business today is the pressure to go for short-term solutions. Many managers complain about the pressure from shareholders and city institutions, leading as it does to less money being spent on research and development. Short-termism is particularly damaging where environmental interests are involved. Water authorities, for example, have in the past been used to building for 60-100 years ahead. Now they are on 5 year plans. If short-termism is to be resisted then the environment must take its place with the other stakeholders which are to be considered alongside the shareholder but not always being overridden by them.

## Summary

To sum up: I have suggested that the engineers' code with its cardinal principle of concern for the public interest should today regard environmental considerations as of the same importance as health and safety factors. There is a public interest, grounded in moral conviction, for the protection of the environment and the conservation of non-renewable resources. I have also maintained that economic development, crucially in the Third World, has no less of a moral claim, hence the title *Sustainable Development*, with all the tension and ambiguity that that phrase suggests.

The particular contribution of engineers to the public interest concerns their unique role in being alert at any stage of a proposed project to its impact on the environment, being able to assess the risks and inform those involved. Scientific rigour has a particular contribution to make in the public debate, but if there is to be a presupposition, it should be one in favour of environmental protection.

Secondly there is the vocation, the high calling and at this point one is almost inescapably drawn towards religious language – for engineers to come up with innovative solutions, involving all their ingenuity and creativity; but which will involve the will to do this as much as the imagination with which to do it. Then finally in the never ending tug between ethical and economic factors, I have suggested that it is not only inevitable but absolutely proper that a balance has to be struck and that engineers will play a key role in ensuring on any particular scheme that it is struck in the right place. I believe that engineers have already gone a long way towards ensuring that the environment is given proper consideration. I refer to the *International Code of Environmental Ethics for Engineers*, a code which is brief but admirably to the point. The Code of Professional Practice, *Engineers in the Environment*, drawn up by the Engineering Council came into effect on 14 March last year. The accompanying *Guidelines on Environmental Issues* is as useful a booklet as you will find anywhere and could well be distributed more widely outside the engineering profession. The further question arises however as to whether it would help the implementation of these codes and guidelines if the Engineering Council and other engineering bodies discussed possible targets. One of the main conclusions of the recent House of Lords Report was that targets are necessary. They were referring to national targets which are politically realistic. But what they write about the national scene is equally applicable to any profession or company.

> "Targets can give policy a clearer sense of direction; they can add to the pace of policy implementation and development; and they can make explicit those aspects of policy which might otherwise remain opaque."

I am delighted that this Conference is taking place because, for the reasons I have mentioned, I believe that engineers have not only a special responsibility but a key role to play in Sustainable Development.

## Questions to the Right Reverend Richard Harries

### Sir Martin Holdgate CB

You mentioned the need for a will to make progress but one of the problems surely is the universality of the will or how much common will there needs to be especially in a highly competitive world. Surely building of consensus through good communication is a crucial part of this and it's very difficult in a society with so many strands to it especially between here and other parts of the world. You might like to reflect further on that?

### Dr Harries

Yes, we have to build a consensus and if there is no consensus there will be no public will. I take it that consensus is built up in a whole range of different ways through fiscal instruments, through legislative instruments, thorough education, through this kind of conference. There is a whole range of ways; the whole mood of society is gradually being changed. I think we can all take heart from the fact that we are so much more aware now than we were even 10 years ago. I think eventually awareness does engender the will. But I think that if that will is going to be engendered in society as a whole it does in the end depend on fairly clear and firm leadership; a real will from certain pioneering spirits and pioneering institutions as we have seen already.

### Nick Cooke British Nuclear Fuels plc

Following the last question when both the questioner and yourself spoke of the importance of building a consensus, how compatible is that with the adversarial system in the courts, parliaments, and public enquiries that you mentioned? Is the British adversarial system incapable of improvement or incapable of change to make building consensus better?

### Dr Harries

Although we all get very frustrated with the English adversarial system I think I am in the end a believer in it. I suppose because I have a pretty strong doctrine of human corruption and human corruptibility. When you get two opposing sides putting their point of view they are much more likely to actually get at the truth of things rather than having one omnicompetent mind surveying it. I mean self interest and institutional interest is involved in everything and I think that the adversarial system is a good way of getting at the truth. But I don't think that necessarily precludes gradually building up a consensus. The fact of the matter is that in our society we do have a consensus on a whole range of issues. Within Parliament itself, although there is a daily ritual of adversarial exchange, nevertheless once you get down to it there is a consensus over a range of issues. I don't think the two are incompatible.

### Professor Roland Clift OBE FEng University of Surrey

I have to say that I don't share your optimism that the adversarial system ensures that nothing is suppressed. It seems to me that a lot of the time there is a very important component that does get suppressed and that component is uncertainty. The adversarial system acts against admission of uncertainty. And it seems to me that engineers generally have a problem that we are not good enough at admitting what we don't know and can't know and it seems to me that the recognition of uncertainty ought to be more central in the precautionary principle than it appears to be at the moment.

**Dr Harries**

Well thank you. I think that I just want to say thank you for that comment which clearly needs to be heard.

**Donald Bruce** Church of Scotland

I just echo again that last comment. On the radio Sir John Houghton was interviewed for Radio 4's Today programme a few days ago about what the predictions are for the impact on certain parts of the world of global warming. He said "I'm afraid we can't be that certain". The reporter said "But we want to know. You say you can't tell me". I thought yes, that is at the heart of the question. Our experience of running working groups in the Church of Scotland is that the more you sit round the table and hear each other the less you get the polarisation that wants an instant answer as that interview implied.

**Dr Harries**

Yes, I think that is excellent and all I would want to add is the particular contribution of engineers to go on digging away for the facts; and not only engineers but all kinds of people who are involved scientifically in the environment. Actually a recognition of how uncertain we are can build a kind of bond which motivates one more strongly to find out more. I think I would want to stress again the necessity of pursuing rigorously the scientific aspect of this.

# Session One
# The Expectations
# of Society

## Rapporteur

Professor Anthony Kelly CBE FEng FRS
Distinguished Research Fellow
University of Cambridge

## Personal Profile

**Professor Anthony Kelly** returned to this country in 1958 from a research post in the USA, to become one of the founding fellows of Churchill College, Cambridge. Following research and teaching at Cambridge, he joined the Scientific Civil Service and became Deputy Director of the National Physical Laboratory, before working for ICI for a number of years. He recently retired from the Vice-Chancellorship of the University of Surrey as the longest serving VC of a UK University, and returned full time to his Fellowship at Churchill.

While at Surrey he founded and managed the Surrey Research Park, one of the leading University Research Parks in Europe. During this period he came into close contact with the construction industry, and in 1989 he took over the Chairmanship of SCOSS (Standing Committee on Structural Safety).

Professor Kelly is a materials scientist/engineer, well known for his work on composite materials. He is a Fellow of the Royal Society, a Fellow of The Royal Academy of Engineering, a Foreign Associate of the US National Academy of Engineering, and holder of a number of international prizes. He is presently Distinguished Research Fellow in the Department of Materials Science at Cambridge and a non-Executive Director of Johnson Wax Ltd and of NPL Management Ltd.

# The Expectations of Society

## Rapporteur's Summary

### Professor Anthony Kelly CBE FEng FRS

I have been asked to summarise the morning's deliberations within five minutes.

Of the physical factors affecting Sustainable Development, the production and usage of energy, both in total and *per capita* (the latter, in the developed world) is the great engine that must be controlled. Energy consumes resources, pollutes and provides a wonderfully comfortable existence. That fact should be stated by all of the speakers and it was implicit in all of the presentations.

Second, the question of Sustainable Development is a global one – all agreed. That the engineer has an indispensable role was equally recognised and so, in a sense, one aim of this conference is already achieved. Technology has provided and it has polluted. To paraphrase Job, technology gives and technology has taken away (amenity). Blessed be the name of technology.

All agreed on what is meant by Sustainable Development – it was the Brundtland definition: development meeting the needs of the present without compromising the ability of future generations to meet their own needs. None questioned this definition.

The need for a good definition for any important task was brought home to me when talking in some detail with Neil Armstrong, the first man on the moon. He was asked what the most important lesson was that he had learned from his moon experience which he could apply to his business (which has been very successful).

He said that President Kennedy gave us the task – clearly defined and with a time scale. "To get a man safely to the moon and back within ten years".

This conference will have succeeded if it can give a similar succinct definition of the task requiring action.

The expectations of society are essentially decided by the consumer: either through his purchases or are reflected in the policies of an elected government.

What has emerged is the need for a directive to the politician, when in power, to define realisable targets with time scales and to seek practical solutions – sharply focused and sensitive to the test of social equity.

The beneficial effects of good legislation, e.g. the *Clean Air Act*, were noted and approved by all.

All agreed that a transparent, accessible and fair (I cannot say neutral) information flow is essential – some called this education. In the process of providing information, the British adversarial system was questioned as not being useful when uncertainty is involved.

Communication meant to most speakers, unravelling the complexities of technical problems so that the consumer (the voter) choice becomes informed and so silly and or environmentally damaging or wasteful solutions are avoided, and sustainable ones advanced and exaggeration eschewed. But two speakers seemed blind to the need for the consumer in the rich countries to be reminded continually (by information flow) of the needs of the poor and of those in less developed lands where the poor are concentrated. That communication must always be open and informed.

An informed public will do more with less. An important phrase, emerging some five years ago. And an informed public will relate rightheadedly to technology. They will know technology. One cannot love what one does not know, we are told. In the same vein, one cannot know what one does not love. We must learn to love and to reverence technology for what it gives and so to learn to guide it well. Ms Ruddock wishes that we also love technologists – an attitude which we in The Academy heartily welcome.

We were told that Bankers are used to taking risks with other people's money – we must respect the words of the Chairman of the High Street Bank. I find that attitude right and proper – it's when Bankers take risks with my money that I object!!

The suggestion that Bankers be well informed and constrain their lending to rightly conceived environmental projects and are prepared to give guidelines for these was very encouraging and the specific suggestion for more venture capital to aid small environmentally innovative businesses is a good suggestion for action at the end of the meeting.

The rest of the meeting will again emphasize the need for targets to measure action – specifically designed targets and practical solutions. I repeat, sharply focused and sensitive to social equity and the global scene. A point made clearly by our Churchman and it will return again in Ziebart's and Hills' talks and in others.

Christian Churchmen usually remind us of ten points – ours today had only three! He said that the Environment must be put beside Health and Safety as another boundary condition for acceptable activity. That is the focus of the conference.

# Keynote Speech
# Sustainable Development and Competitiveness

## Speaker

The Rt Hon Ian Lang MP
President of the Board of Trade

## Personal Profile

**The Rt Hon Ian Lang** was born in Glasgow in 1940 and entered Parliament as the Member of Parliament for Galloway in May 1979 and has been MP for Galloway and Upper Nithsdale since June 1983.

He was a member of the Parliamentary Select Committee on Scottish Affairs from 1979 to 1981. A former vice-chairman of the Scottish Conservative and Unionist Party and Assistant Government Whip and Lord Commissioner of the Treasury, Mr Lang was appointed Parliamentary Under Secretary of State at the Department of Employment in February 1986. He joined The Scottish Office in September of that year.

From September 1986 until June 1987 Mr Lang was Minister for Industry and Home Affairs. He became Minister of State at The Scottish Office in June 1987, with responsibility for Industry and Local Government. He was also the Minister responsible for Highlands and Islands, Training, Tourism and the Arts.

Between July 1989 and September 1990 he was responsible for Industry and Education.

Ian Lang become Secretary of State for Scotland in November 1990 and was appointed President of the Board of Trade on 5 July 1995.

Mr Lang was educated at Lathallan School, Montrose, Rugby School and Sidney Sussex College, Cambridge, graduating in 1962. He was an insurance broker before entering Parliament and held a number of directorships.

# Sustainable Development and Competitiveness

## The Rt Hon Ian Lang MP

## Introduction

It is a great pleasure for me to be here to speak about Sustainable Development: what it means for industry; the Government's strategy to achieve it, and the opportunities that it creates.

And I want to emphasise the crucial contribution that engineers in industry and academia must make if sustainable development is to be a reality.

What is "Sustainable Development"?

On the one hand, all societies want to achieve economic development to secure higher standards of living, now and for future generations. On the other hand, they also seek to protect and enhance their environment, now and for their children. Sustainable Development tries to reconcile these two objectives to provide "development that meets the needs of the present generation without compromising the ability of future generations to meet their own needs".

The scale of the challenge is awe-inspiring. The 21st century will see a doubling of the current global population, combined with increasing demands for a better quality of life. Simply doubling our own efficiency in the use of our planet's natural resources, even if it were that easy, would be nothing like sufficient. Huge leaps in vision, in technology and in attitude are needed.

## Sustainable Development as a Business Opportunity

So what does Sustainable Development mean for business? Companies will increasingly find that environmental factors will influence their business decisions. There will, for example, be increasing controls on what companies can discharge to the environment, and the costs of waste disposal will rise. Those companies who recognise this and integrate environmental factors into their business strategies will see Sustainable Development as an opportunity and will be able to take advantage of it.

For many sectors, the drive to achieve Sustainable Development will give rise to new products and services. The resulting opportunities for the UK environmental industry in world markets are immense. The market today for environmental technologies is worth over $200 billion. It is expected to rise to over $500 billion by 2010, as developed as well as developing countries alike continue to realise their need for the best advice and technologies available.

The UK is already a significant player, with a trade surplus of $350 million a year. But we cannot rest on our laurels. British businesses need to grasp the opportunities to provide innovative products and services in order to build on our success.

Yet even with clear market opportunities, Sustainable Development cannot happen on its own. It needs active and widespread support; after all, everyone has a role to play in making the most efficient use of the planet's resources.

## Role of Government

That is why the Government is committed to integrating Sustainable Development into its policies, and why we have developed our Sustainable Development strategy, to set the framework to encourage sustainability in the UK.

Let me give three quick examples drawn from the strategy.

First, we are setting a clear framework of policy and effective regulation that is sensitive to the needs of the business community. For instance, our 10 to 15 year long term strategies for solid waste and air quality will help industry to plan its investments to take advantage of the opportunities that Sustainable Development can bring.

Second, we are studying how to make more use of economic instruments. The landfill tax is one example of this.

Third, we are improving and extending our dialogue with industry on longer term environmental trends.

I am sure that you are also aware of the Government's *Technology Foresight* exercise, to which The Royal Academy of Engineering so ably and constructively contributed. In identifying the technologies to meet market needs over the next 10-20 years, *Technology Foresight* has recognised the need for a cleaner, more sustainable world as one of its six overriding strategic themes.

At a more general level, the Government also has a vital role in maintaining the economy, and in developing a trading environment, in which enterprise and excellence can flourish. That is why, for example, we are working to achieve access to open and competitive markets on a global scale. Through breakthroughs such as the *Energy Charter Treaty*, we are encouraging other nations to take measures such as ensuring that energy prices reflect their true costs. This will help to avoid the type of environmental problems now being faced in the former eastern bloc – a stark demonstration of how economic stagnation and environmental degradation so often go hand in hand.

## Challenge for Engineers

The Government can set the climate for more liberal trade, and for innovation. But it is not the Government's job to apply the concepts of Sustainable Development to real processes and products. That is a job for UK businesses, and in those businesses, engineers have a crucial role to play in bringing Sustainable Development from vision to reality.

I would like to say at this point how highly I, and my Government colleagues, value the strength and reputation of science and engineering in Britain. Your disciplines are key assets for the UK. You have the ability to develop processes and products which are not only significantly more environmentally friendly than those of today but which are also economic and practical.

You can develop and implement the principles of process engineering. You can apply the younger sciences of biotechnology and life cycle analysis to develop new manufacturing processes. Through environmentally-sensitive design, you can minimise a product's environmental impact during manufacturing, everyday use, and at the end of its life. You can identify solutions which reduce our needs for scarce resources, minimise the amount of waste we produce, and deal with the pollution problems of the past. You can do all this while maintaining price, performance and quality standards.

## Cleaner Technology and Competitiveness

Developing and using cleaner technologies need not necessarily mean increased costs for business. There are plenty of case studies which show that relatively small changes to a process can yield significant benefits to a company's competitiveness as well as to the environment.

For example, *Project Catalyst* in the Mersey Basin, part funded by the Department of Trade and Industry, identified nearly 400 ways of reducing waste in the 14 companies that took part. Over 100 measures have been implemented already, leading to annual saving of over £2 million. If all 400 were taken up, the companies would save some £8 million a year.

Most of these measures were not radical breakthroughs. They depended on the application of existing technologies, many of which have already been adopted by the most forward looking companies. Getting this message across to many sectors of UK industry, and to small companies in particular, is one of the key activities of the Environmental Technology Best Practice Programme, funded by DTI together with the Department of the Environment. It aims to raise environmental standards in industry, as an integral part of improving industrial competitiveness. Waste minimisation and the adoption of cost effective cleaner technologies are permanent themes of the programme, which aims to achieve annual net cost savings for industry of at least £160 million in the longer term.

Even though much can be achieved with existing technologies, we still need even cleaner and more cost effective processes and products. Indeed, in immediate response to the report of the Technology Foresight steering group, the Engineering and Physical Sciences Research Council and DTI jointly announced a major new £11 million package of grant support aimed at waste minimisation in industry. It includes a new LINK programme and a Teaching Company Scheme programme. These will bring together chemical, process, and materials engineers from industry and academia, working together to develop cleaner processes and products.

We need to ensure the uptake of these new processes and products. Our universities are key drivers in ensuring that people entering the business and research communities are aware of the potential. I am delighted that The Royal Academy of Engineering has achieved so much success with its programme to appoint *Visiting Professors in the Principles of Engineering Design*, and proud that the DTI has been able to offer assistance. I understand that the work of a significant number of the Visiting Professors is relevant to Sustainable Development. I see this as an excellent indication of the importance that The Academy attaches to this topic.

Of course, our competitors are also considering the need to engineer for Sustainable Development. Forging links between engineers here and overseas can lead to major advantages. The *Engineers to Japan Scheme*, administered by The Academy on DTI's behalf, is one example of how our experts can learn about overseas developments. Because of its success, we are developing a successor scheme, to cover more countries and more disciplines.

Recognising the achievements of engineers, and the contribution they can make to Sustainable Development, is vital. Engineers are the people who will make the practical and visible difference. But the public tends to take their enormous contribution for granted. Challenging this lack of appreciation is just one of the tasks facing the engineering community's *Action for Engineering* initiative. This initiative aims to increase the influence of engineers, and increase the recognition of their achievements. Through conferences like this one, and its participation in the *Action for Engineering* initiative, The Academy is playing a key role in achieving this.

## Conclusion

Let me conclude. Sustainable Development holds massive opportunities for industry. The Government must, of course, set the policy and regulatory framework and foster an economic climate that enables innovation. But the challenge to realise Sustainable Development rests ultimately with industry. And it is for you – the UK's industrialists, scientists and engineers – to respond to the challenge if we are to make progress.

Those who argue that we cannot have economic growth and a sustainable environment are undervaluing the contribution and ingenuity of the engineering profession. But make no mistake, the challenges for engineers and for industry are both formidable and urgent. This conference is seeking to identify specific actions to help make Sustainable Development a reality. For all our sakes, I wish you success.

THE ROYAL ACADEMY OF ENGINEERING

# Engineering for Sustainable Development

## S E S S I O N   T W O

### The Challenge for Manufacturing

**Chairman** Stewart Miller CBE FEng
**Rapporteur** Professor Roland Clift OBE FEng

**Novel Products:**
**More from Less, More Efficiently**
Sir Ronald Hampel

**Automotive Design for**
**Environmental Protection**
Dr-Ing Wolfgang Ziebart

**Sustainable Product Lifecycles**
Dr Peter White

# Session Two
# The Challenge for Manufacturing

**Chairman**

Stewart Miller CBE FEng
Director, Engineering & Technology
Rolls-Royce plc

## Introduction

The response by engineers to society's expectations for protection of the environment has been significant, but all will acknowledge that much more remains to be done. Manufacturing industry has responsibility to improve its own operations, to develop the design of its products and to reduce their environmental impact throughout their life cycle.

This session of the conference aims to illustrate all these aspects through the activites of three large international companies, covering chemical, automotive and consumer products. From the industry point of view, work on sustainable development has to be integrated into the overall task of management and has to make business as well as environmental sense.

## Personal Profile

**Stewart Miller** was appointed Director, Engineering and Technology of Rolls-Royce plc on 1 January 1993, having previously been Managing Director – Aerospace Group. He has been a member of the Board of Rolls-Royce plc since October 1985.

He was educated at Kirkcaldy High School and Edinburgh University, where he graduated in Mechanical Engineering. He joined Rolls-Royce in 1954. After a graduate apprenticeship, he spent a number of years on technology work, specialising in combustion. Subsequently, he took charge of a number of Advanced Engineering programmes, and spent a period in the design of new projects. From 1976 until 1984 he was associated with the RB211-535 engine for the Boeing 757, as Chief Engineer and then Head of Project. He was in charge of all aero-engine design and development from 1985 to 1990 and is now board member for engineering and technology across the company.

Stewart Miller is a Fellow of The Royal Academy of Engineering, a Fellow of the Royal Aeronautical Society, and a Fellow of the Institution of Mechanical Engineers. He was awarded the British Gold Medal of the Royal Aeronautical Society in 1988 and an honorary Doctorate of Technology by Loughborough University of Technology in 1992. He is Pro-Chancellor of Loughborough University of Technology and a visiting professor at the University of Strathclyde. He is a member of the Engineering and Physical Sciences Research Council, and has led the Innovative Manufacturing Initiative of EPSRC, BBSRC and ESRC from the start and is chairman of the management committee.

# Novel Products: More from Less, More Efficiently

**Sir Ronald Hampel**

Chairman, ICI plc

## Personal Profile

**Sir Ronald Hampel** became Chairman of Imperial Chemicals Industries plc in April 1995. He had been Deputy Chairman and Chief Executive since May 1993, following the demerger of the bioscience activities into ZENECA plc, and was formerly Chief Operating Officer (since 1991). He joined the ICI Board in 1985 and until 1991 was the Director with territorial responsibility for the Americas. He had previously held business portfolios on the Board for Explosives, Paints, Specialities, Polyurethanes and Tioxide, and been responsible for Acquisitions and Divestments.

Sir Ronald graduated in Modern Languages and Law at Cambridge. He was knighted in the 1995 New Year Honours.

# Novel Products: More from Less, More Efficiently
## Sir Ronald Hampel

## Introduction

I am confident that there is not one of us here today who does not applaud the concept of Sustainable Development. In the now classic book of the World Commission on Environment and Development entitled *Our Common Future*, Sustainable Development is described as a process of change in which the exploitation of resources, the direction of investments, the orientation of technological development and institutional change are made consistent with the future as well as the present needs. In its broadest sense the strategy for Sustainable Development is to promote harmony among human beings and between humanity and nature. As our Secretary of State John Gummer so neatly puts it, "We should not steal from our children". I can subscribe to that and I am sure you can too.

Although it might be easy to describe Sustainable Development it is another matter altogether to comprehend how such a far reaching goal can be advanced. There has to be the development of a technological, political and social organisation to make way for a new era of economic growth which overcomes poverty through meeting essential needs and an assurance that the poor get their fair share of resources. This change must come about.

As a global society we are living like wayward aristocrats. Instead of living comfortably on the interest of our capital we are consuming the inheritance of future generations by jeopardising that capital which is the very world around us. It is the very thing we depend on for our survival – minerals, trees, soil, food. We can be accused, without second thoughts, that we are eroding our children's natural capital.

Whether one agrees with this view of the world is neither here nor there. This idea is taken seriously by politicians the world over and the United Nations Commission on Sustainable Development is dedicated to its advancement. Sustainable Development is already reflected in global treaties and will, increasingly, be reflected in the laws that govern society and the way we run our businesses.

The issue has to be taken seriously. Global society has indicated quite clearly that it wants the future to be sustainable – very important given the increasing population of the world. We are all a part of that society and we cannot choose a different path.

In making Sustainable Development work we can perhaps understand the requirements:

- a political system that secures democratic decision making
- an economic system that is able to generate surpluses
- a social system that provides for solutions to tensions
- a production system that recognises the importance of preservation of the ecological base for development
- a technological system that can search continuously for new solutions
- an international system that fosters sustainable patterns of trade
- a finance and administrative system that is flexible and has a capacity for self correction.

But how can they possibly be put into practice? I think it is fair to say that nobody really knows how, because it is going to require a huge and fundamental shift in the way we run our lives, our businesses, our industries, societies and economies. It is a challenge for this and the next century.

The complexity of the issue cannot be offered as an excuse for doing nothing.

So what can industry and individual companies actually do today to move the process forward and effectively play their part? I believe there are three key steps that we can take now:

- participation in the debate
- using innovation and technology to develop new products and processes with reduced environmental impact
- the introduction of target driven management systems to ensure continuous environmental improvement.

## Participation in the Debate

Let me address my first point. Industry must participate along with the rest of society in the Debate about how everyone can reach the goal. No more sitting on the sidelines. We must be part of the process and our input must be positive. In my company we are actively implementing the International Chamber of Commerce's *Business Charter for Sustainable Development*, which is a part of our Safety Health and Environment Policy, we support fully the proactive position of the International Council of Chemical Associations (ICCA) on Sustainable Development and we are an active member of the World Business Council for Sustainable Development. Here, in the UK, we are a corporate member of the United Nations Environment and Development – UK Committee.

## Eco-efficiency

My second point is that, until the grand plan is formulated and there has been a paradigm shift in the way the world works, we must improve our eco-efficiency by reducing our impact on the environment in as many ways as we can and design products and processes that, in turn, help others to reduce their environmental impact too.

In my company we have a simple, straightforward approach to realising and implementing the concept of Sustainable Development. We apply our innovative, scientific, technological and engineering skills to produce new products with lower environmental impact and more product from less raw material, more efficiently.

It is always good to talk about success and in ICI we have made very significant strides in improving our environmental performance over the last five years by working towards a series of tough, challenging objectives that we set ourselves in 1990. Most significant has been the reduction in hazardous wastes by over 80 per cent such that they now represent just four per cent of our total waste stream. Non-hazardous wastes to air and water are both close to our 50 per cent reduction goal and energy efficiency has improved each year. We are proud of these achievements which is a reflection of the dedication of everyone in ICI. But the job is far from over. There is still a lot to do. Our achievements to date only keep us abreast of the contemporary world. To remain competitive we must continue to make further strides to meet future demands.

I am reasonably optimistic that we will solve the pollution abatement issues in manufacture. In most cases, the technology required is known, or can be developed. The issue is much more with the speed with which the problems can be settled and the standards we wish to achieve. The standards will inevitably tighten, but there is at some point a cost/benefit trade off to be resolved. An exemplar is our chlorine and caustic soda operations at Runcorn. Brine is pumped by pipe from the salt deposits in Cheshire. A proportion of the brine is converted by electrolysis into chlorine and caustic soda and the remainder is released into the sea after treatment to remove all but the most minor traces of hazardous materials. Currently there are no practical ways to change this method of operation and in our view any possible environmental benefits brought by a change, such as the construction of a new pipeline to return the brine to the salt deposits as a closed loop system, would be minimal and insignificant whereas the cost would be very high, tens of millions of pounds, and not justified. We must spend our money judiciously to get the best and maximum environmental benefit.

## Developing New Products

The focus of attention is now switching to considering the potential impact of environmental considerations on the development of new products and services. This switch is increasingly driving environmental thinking to the early design stage rather than as an afterthought at the end of the development programme and it is fast becoming a major competitive opportunity for an innovative company such as ICI.

There are significant rewards available for those who understand the issues and who develop products and services with lower environmental impact to meet the needs ahead of competitors. This also provides new product markets and opportunities for new relationships between customers and suppliers which will be yet another source of competitive advantage. We recognise the importance of these emerging opportunities in my company and have organised our major research, technology and engineering talents within the businesses to work close to the marketplace and respond quickly to our customers' needs.

There is absolutely no doubt that innovation is essential in tackling the issues and bringing about positive change with a move to a more sustainable environment. The first reaction of any technical company faced with an environmental issue has, in the past, been an attempt to solve it by the application of hardware and capital. I believe that this approach has less and less relevance today. The answer, more often than not, lies in something more simple: the recycling of a by-product stream, an improvement in process efficiency, the redesign of a process. Although it is engineers and scientists who contributed to our problems by continuing to use processes and products that fit the norms of another era, it is now the job of the engineers and scientists to help us find innovative solutions better suited to the pressures of the 21st Century. It is recognised that industry has a key role to play in Sustainable Development. It is we who are charged with the task of creating the wealth to underwrite the changes required. It is also recognised that true innovation cannot be hurried, nor must it be stifled by the imposition of restrictive legislation. Regulation alone is not sufficient to drive progress.

The chemical industry is a major industrial sector and an essential contributor to welfare and employment on a global scale. Its long term future must be rooted in a dynamic policy, whereby continual innovation results in an increase of productivity which underpins continued international competitiveness as a pre-requisite of sustainable job creation. It has a clear role to play and has already demonstrated how it can respond to issues and play its part in an increasingly environmentally aware society.

There are numerous examples which I can quote from ICI. The most striking was the successful development of our new ozone benign KLEA product range to replace CFCs and HCFCs in refrigeration and air-conditioning across all sectors of industry in record breaking time. We mobilised over 100 people from the business of ICI into a project team which included experts in catalysis, analytical sciences, environment, process technology and manufacturing, backed by the impressive capabilities of our engineers. By halving the normal development time for such a project we played our part in allowing CFC phase-out dates under the terms of the Montreal Protocol to be pulled back from the year 2000 and beyond to the end of 1995. We are now a world leader in the alternatives to CFCs and have plants in the UK, US and Japan to meet the increasing world demand and I was very proud that the KLEA Team was recognised by The Royal Academy of Engineering when they received the MacRobert Award in 1994.

This is just one example from ICI. There is a raft of new products and processes from ICI which include:

1. The reuse and recycling of PET and Acrylics. A new product range of packaging film has been introduced in the USA called Melinex ECO which includes PET that comes from over 44 million discarded soft drink bottles that would otherwise have gone to landfill: and in the UK we have launched a scheme called *Recovery* to recycle scrap acrylic sheet from customers back to high grade product.

2. ICI Polyurethanes has developed *Waterlily*, a comfort cushioning foam which is blown by water – steam – instead of CFCs. It has also developed a range of sustainable building products using small amounts of MDI to bind agricultural waste such as wood, straw and sugar bagasse into strong, waterproof building boards. These new products have particular importance in the developing world.

3. Our waterborne paint production technology now incorporates the latest computerisation to enable our production facilities to have zero liquid effluent. ICI Paints also won a Queen's Award for the Environment in 1995 for Aquabase paint for the vehicle refinish industry offering our customers the option to reduce volatile organic emissions by over 70 per cent.

4. Tioxide has spent over £200 million since 1990 to reduce its environmental impact throughout the world and to turn wastes into saleable products. Liquid acidic wastes are now neutralised to form solid gypsum (calcium sulphate) which is sold to the building and paper industries and to farmers as a soil conditioner. Other co-products include carbon dioxide for the beer and beverage industries and iron salts for the water treatment industry. Indeed, 580,000 tonnes of these products were sold in 1994 and we hope this will increase as new markets are developed.

5. Our PTA production process is just one example which demonstrates how our scientists and engineers have been able over time, to bring about real improvements in reducing raw material requirements and improving energy efficiency. ICI has produced pure terephthalic acid (PTA) since 1967 when it first commissioned a 36,000 tonnes per annum plant at Wilton. Today, ICI produces close to one million tonnes world-wide and our capacity is growing to meet increasing demand. Over this time our scientists and engineers have continuously developed the production technology to enhance the quality of the product, meet the increasing demands of our customers and improve efficiencies and environmental performance.

Since those early days, energy efficiency has been improved by 75 per cent and raw materials efficiency by 60 per cent. For the year 2000 and beyond we expect to see further improvements in these parameters by 60 per cent and 30 per cent over 1995. This clearly represents a demanding challenge but new ideas are abundant and the technical team is well resourced. The trick will be to select and pursue the winners. This is a clear example of a win-win situation. ICI is a winner in the competitive race and the environment benefits too.

Our scientists are also looking to the longer term. Each year ICI invests over £5 million in an extensive programme of collaborations and projects with academia world-wide thereby ensuring that we remain at the forefront of scientific thinking and development.

In the environmental area, we have 8 major collaborations at universities in the UK, Australia, Belgium and the Netherlands investigating subjects that include modelling of recycling, life cycle analysis, and petrochemical feedstock recovery. ICI is also leading a consortium of companies and universities to look at the potential of sustainable biosynthetic feedstocks such as sucrose as the basic building block for new polymeric packaging materials, paints and insulating products. This £5 million project is being funded through SUSTEC.

## Correct Management Systems

I now return to my third and final point – that it is essential to create the correct management systems which are integrated into the company's overall management structure and ensure that goals are established, resources allocated, performance monitored and corrective action taken as required. They must encourage innovation and continuous improvement and promote a change in established cultures to help the company meet the new demands and pressures of the future.

In ICI we tie our safety, health and environmental management scheme to the theme of continuous improvement. We therefore set goals and measure all progress towards them and as we get close, set new goals and so on.

We started our environmental management by requiring everyone in the ICI Group to report to the centre on compliance with existing emission consents, environmental incidents, public complaints and environmental improvement plans. No manager likes to report no progress. Just by turning the spotlight on these issues, we achieved some improvement.

We stepped up the pace of improvement in 1990 when I and my colleagues on the Executive Team set clear goals – a world-wide standard for new plant construction, an objective in energy efficiency, one in recycling and a 50 per cent waste reduction target. These established that we were not looking for only incremental improvements, but a step change.

We meant business!

I have already described the progress we are making against these objectives and we have already met at least some of our targets ahead of schedule. I believe that the time is now opportune to build on the improvements that we have already made and set new targets to take us into the next millennium. I am convinced that we will benefit by combining environmental improvement with safety and health so I have introduced new targets in these areas as well. This new set of targets will be called our *SHE Challenge 2000*. As with our previous set of objectives they will be demanding on our businesses but they are attainable. Our achievements towards these targets will be one of our main contributions to the world-wide Chemical Industries *Responsible Care* programme.

We will be launching the targets under the banner of *SHE Challenge 2000* in the next few days but allow me to briefly allude to our overall goals.

*In Safety,* I have set new, tough demands to sustain the annual reduction in injury rates achieved over the last few years. Our long term goal is zero harm to people as a result of our activities. For this to occur it will be necessary for our sites and departments to go for long periods without injury to staff. There will be no room for poor performers. We are now a Safety leader among European chemical companies but we want to be the best in the world.

*In Occupational Health,* we have developed performance measures to assess progress and work is in hand to define these further. A major area of development is the fuller understanding of occupational health protection by line management, and its consequent ownership as a line, rather than functional accountability. Achievement of the targets we are setting will give us a leadership position among the world chemical companies.

*In Environment,* I have instructed the businesses to build on the solid foundations of our existing set of environmental objectives while taking into account the developments in legislation and world thinking on Sustainable Development. While continuing towards our goal of zero spills and 100 per cent compliance with our allowed releases, we will reduce emissions further with special emphasis being placed on reducing overall environmental impact of our operations. We are developing better procedures to assess priorities for actions to achieve substantial environmental improvements. There will be reductions in releases of key substances to air and to water and we will continue to improve energy efficiency and use of resources.

Finally we will be allying all this to the products we make and sell through securing a leadership position in product stewardship for the management of the SHE impact of all our products from their development through production, storage, transport, use and final disposal.

This concept is already well established across ICI: some of our businesses are world leaders – but we need to extend this to embrace each and every business.

We must seek continuous improvement in all areas. The challenge will not be easy.

## A Sustainable Future

I hope I have demonstrated that ICI takes its environmental responsibilities very seriously and sees good SHE performance as essential to the long term success of the company. While the nirvana of complete global Sustainable Development may still be far away we recognise that we, as an international company, have a key role to play in helping others in reaching the common goal – a sustainable future. What better way than leading by example?

# Automotive Design for Environmental Protection

**Dr-Ing Wolfgang Ziebart**

Director, 3 Series

BMW AG

## Personal Profile

**Dr Wolfgang Ziebart** studied engineering at the Munich Technical University.

In 1977 he joined BMW on a one year training program in the Product Development department. On completion of the trainee program he was appointed a design engineer in the body pre-program group between 1978-1981. He worked on various concept studies rising to the position of section leader. He then headed up a group of engineers attached to manufacturing with the task of trouble shooting on the various assembly lines.

In 1983, Dr Ziebart was nominated Executive Engineer, body preprogram design. In 1985 he transferred to the heating, air conditioning and ventilation department as Chief Engineer. Following, a company reorganisation in 1986 he became Chief Engineer of the Electric/Electronics Department, one of the biggest in BMW employing approximately 330 engineers engaged in design & testing of all electric/electronic components from headlamp wiring looms to car radios. In 1982 body engineering was added to his responsibilities which meant approximately 1 000 engineers were under his direction.

In 1993 Dr Ziebart was assigned to his current position as Director of BMW 3 series vehicle line where he is responsible for the complete vehicle, engineering, production, finance controlling, purchase and product marketing.

# Automotive Design for Environmental Protection
## Dr-Ing Wolfgang Ziebart

## Introduction

The main challenges and highlights in both the development and production of new automobiles have changed significantly. While only a few years ago product-specific features such as engine output, dimensions, or styling were still decisive, the principal objective today is to find modern solutions catering for the increasingly environment-oriented demands made by both customers and society as a whole. It is no longer size and power as a purpose in themselves, but rather intelligent solutions serving to preserve resources without making concessions in terms of quality and functions that count today and give us our targets for the future. We need solutions offering the best all-round achievement in the overall context of mobility, environmental protection and economy.

With this in mind, please allow me to offer you a somewhat broader perspective in this presentation – especially as we at BMW have for a long time seen our responsibility for the environment not only in terms of our products. I will therefore refer to the overall life-cycle of an automobile, ranging from production through the actual use of the car all the way to recycling. In addition, I will show you briefly how we envisage an energy strategy pointing into the future on the basis of regenerating forms of energy, and in conclusion I will point out why we regard all these measures as absolutely essential in order to preserve our mobility as individuals and in society as a whole.

The fact nevertheless remains that our responsibility versus the environment is only one side of the coin – the other is the responsibility we, as an economic enterprise, owe our shareholders and workforce. Indeed, these two factors are by no means a contradiction in terms at BMW!

Facing international competition more than virtually any other industry, it is of course essential for us to focus on aspects of cost, quality and time, in this way becoming efficient and successful. But this is not enough for the future. In fact, such qualities must be taken for granted in order to remain competitive. We are really convinced that to be successful in future, an agile corporation must also show a high level of social competence. We all face the great challenge to consider social currents and adjust accordingly through our products, our corporate culture, and the very 'look' of our companies. The focus today and far into the future is on the responsibility a company shows for the environment. We are convinced that both today and to a far greater extent in future, particularly young consumers will refuse to buy products from, or work for, companies which are not environmentally conscious.

Looking at the question of environmental compatibility, we therefore apply this criterion at BMW, as I mentioned before, to the entire life-cycle of our products, that is from production through actual use all the way to recycling or waste management.

More than 20 years ago BMW became one of the first companies in Germany to establish a special department responsible for environmental protection. This was indeed the nucleus from which BMW's environmental management policy has grown over the years. Suffering at an early point in time from the problems of production in a large city, and with interfaces directly connecting our factory with residential areas, the decision-makers at BMW became sensitive to the requirements of environmental protection very early on. Indeed, the consistent application of this policy was then expressed clearly, for example, by our signing of the ICC international environmental charter, and in the early '90s, through the introduction of official environmental protection guidelines by BMW AG requiring all employees on all hierarchical levels within the company to act responsibly and in line with environmental needs and requirements. You might therefore say that environmental protection has become a genuine task of management at BMW. It is the specific responsibility of our executives to implement and live out these environmental guidelines, in this way motivating employees in general to take up and accept this challenge in a positive sense.

Even at the early point of corporate planning, we therefore set the standards for our overall, environment-oriented company policy. The objective is to show decision-makers that all decisions must be taken both in the specific interest of the company and in the interest of society, thus taking social and ecological requirements into account in full. A further point is that BMW, even in the development of new products and production processes, thinks in material cycles, thus considering not only the outgoing, but also the incoming, flow of materials.

## Reduction of Emissions

In production we seek specifically to use all resources with maximum economy – both production materials as well as energy and operating materials – and to avoid emissions of all kinds. Since this subject matter is very complex, however, I can offer you only a few examples at this point:

At the end of the 1960s we decided at our plant in Munich to change over our energy supply from coal to natural gas. Indeed, this decision played a key role in enabling the Munich Municipal Council to link up to the gas network. Today, Munich has the lowest $SO_2$ levels of all German cities. At our other plants we applied the same policy, installing block-type thermal power stations at our plants in Regensburg and Steyr back in the 1980s. The use of such power stations allows us to run our operations at about 85 per cent efficiency on primary energy, compared with about 35 per cent as the normal figure with a conventional power station.

Moving on to our paint shops, we have increased coating efficiency here from 30 per cent back in the 1980s to over 70 per cent today. In the last two years we have been able to increase the non-volatile content of the top coat from 13 to 21 per cent. The result is a considerable reduction in the emission of solvents and the amount of paint sludge. Applying air extraction in order to decontaminate the spraying cells, and using paint driers with fully-integrated thermal afterburning facilities, we have been able to reduce emission levels by 92-95 per cent compared with the levels in 1970. Accordingly, more than 99 per cent of the paint particles are removed from the air extracted from the painting cells. BMW was the first car maker to produce vehicles with metallic water-based paint.

The rinsing water required in this entire process is recirculated. Through the use of such sophisticated recirculation technologies, we have in the last 10 years reduced the amount of water required to produce a car from about 13 cubic metres, which is still the average figure in the motor industry today, to about 2 cubic metres. And for more than 15 years we have been separating oleiferous water physically – not chemically – by using semi-permeable membranes in ultra-filtration plants. All of BMW's factories in Bavaria are equipped with sewage disposal plants which meet the requirements of the 40th Effluent Directive in our latest Water Conservation Act. The final, highly concentrated product obtained in this way can be recycled at waste-oil regeneration plants. Various BMW dealerships are already equipped with coalescent separators for washing car engines and de-waxing new vehicles upon arrival. The very positive result is that absolutely no waste oil or emulsion is able to escape into the sewage system. Yet a further point is that all our production sites are equipped with groundwater gauges used to provide clear records of our operations. The gauges serve to check both groundwater levels and the chemical composition of the water.

BMW is a shareholder and founding member of the Association for the Disposal of Hazardous Waste in Bavaria (GSB). Although the cost of handling hazardous waste was comparatively high to begin with, the dividend generated in this way is now absolutely clear. Over the last 20 years we have paid particular attention to the improvement of material sorting and to the use of environmentally favourable materials. Today, as a result, only about 5 per cent of our waste has to be disposed of through GSB, 15 per cent is household waste, and the remaining 80 per cent can either be recycled or reprocessed. Waste disposal logistics are now planned immediately upon the development of a new production line. All our production plants have buildings and facilities for sorting and preparing waste and scrap. To meet the demands of the future in terms of suitable waste disposal, BMW is currently developing waste disposal logistics that will embrace not only our own production, but also that of our suppliers, ensuring in this way that waste disposal is both environmentally-friendly and economical.

We also focus on noise emission, every BMW site being subject to noise emission calculations. Using computer-simulated models, we are able to examine various layout variations, forecasting noise levels and implementing the optimum solution. A good example of how we have solved even complex logistic, traffic, and noise problems is BMW's central external warehouse (ZAL) in Eching near Munich. In the past the residential areas surrounding the site were plagued at night by the noise of huge trucks delivering parts from our suppliers. Today, the warehouse is supplied directly by freight forwarders and the German Bundesbahn. The trucks required for delivering supplies go straight to our final assembly line at the Munich plant in 10 to 15-minute cycles spread out over a definite period of 16 hours. On their way back the trucks then carry scrap and waste to the central external warehouse, where it is sorted.

To make the actual operation of our vehicles as environmentally efficient as possible, we apply the latest state of the art in the interest of both fuel economy and emissions. As a result, all of our vehicles outperform – in some cases quite substantially – all emission standards worldwide in terms of both noise and exhaust emissions. Just like BMW automobiles, BMW motorcycles are also the forerunners in this area, since this year we are becoming the first manufacturer in the world to offer all our motorcycles with a catalytic converter fitted as standard.

## Reduction of Fuel Consumption

The fuel economy of our models has also improved consistently over the years. As an example, just consider the new 328i able to offer unparalleled economy of 8.5 ltr/100 km or 33.2 mpg Imp in the DIN combined cycle, which is quite unique in the power range up to 150 kW or 204 bhp. The features which make this kind of supreme economy possible are, first, the use of the most innovative technology and fine tuning to the last detail and, second, our achievements in lightweight engineering. Talking about lightweight engineering, I should add at this point that BMW, unlike some other manufacturers, pursues a somewhat different strategy based exclusively on parameters such as "significant weight benefits throughout the entire vehicle", "technology we are able to master" and "customer-relevant benefits", and not on simple gimmicks which may look nice in advertising but do not mean much in practice.

Focusing on the components of a car and the use of, say, aluminium as a particularly light material, we have a clear sequence of priorities starting with the engine, moving on next to the suspension, and only then providing for the use of aluminium in bodyshell construction. Let me emphasise that we do not regard lightweight engineering as a value in itself, but rather as one possible way to save resources in the use of a car, in production and recycling, in this way benefitting both the customer and the environment.

Proceeding according to this sequence of priorities, we first capitalised on the high potential offered by the engine. Switching over our six-cylinder engines to aluminium, for example, we have been able to reduce net engine weight by no less than 31 kg.

We are currently in the process of using the enormous weight-saving potential offered by the suspension, the new generation of our 5 Series to be launched towards the end of this year featuring an all-aluminium suspension more than 50 kg lighter than on the previous model.

Looking at the bodyshell, on the other hand, lightweight engineering the way we see it means continuing to capitalise on the many benefits of steel technology already mastered and proven in large-scale production, instead of exposing the customer to imponderables where a minor weight-saving might easily be offset by other disadvantages.

The new 5 Series clearly proves what an enormous potential for optimisation steel bodyshell technology is still able to offer. By consistently applying computer simulation (FE methods), using specially developed high-strength steel plate, and applying new joining technologies such as laser welding and the most advanced holographic measuring processes, we have created a bodyshell with a standard of stability quite unique in this segment of the market, without the slightest increase in weight. The various bodyshell rigidity measurements on the new model exceed the excellent level already achieved on our current car by up to 50 per cent.

## Vehicle Recycling

Last but certainly not least, BMW applies the same demanding standards to the third phase of a product's life-cycle, that is environmentally-friendly waste management. Instead of creating new problems with new, unproven materials, we have made it our strategy to solve known problems by way of new solutions. With this in mind, our cars excel, for example, by the fact that they are almost totally free of 'problematic' materials and are designed from the outset for optimum recyclability.

BMW has indeed been active for a long time in the area of recycling. We started gaining valuable experience in the re-use of components and materials at an early point, since BMW has been reconditioning used assemblies and aggregates for almost 30 years now, subsequently offering such components to customers as Original BMW Exchange Parts. As early as 1987 we became the first manufacturer to take back used catalytic converters from numerous European countries.

Establishing a pilot dismantling plant for old cars at our Landshut factory, we have been developing and compiling technical know-how ever since 1990 for the proper dismantling, use and recycling of BMW automobiles. As a result, we have been in a position since 1991 to offer customers a take-back guarantee for all old BMWs starting with the model range we had at the time.

Under the guidance of BMW, the Automobile Recycling Project Group established by German carmakers has developed a comprehensive recycling concept which the Association of European Automobile Manufacturers has also joined in the meantime. In late 1991 this concept was presented to the EU Commission with the target to standardise the rules for recycling old cars throughout Europe, in this way establishing cross-border and cross-industry material cycles. Today, BMW represents all German car manufacturers in the End-of-Life-Vehicles Working Party of the European Commission in Brussels.

Regrettably, however, politics is a slow and sluggish business. The rapid development of a full-coverage network of old car recyclers BMW is seeking to achieve is still obstructed by the absence of laws and statutory principles. But BMW has remained active nevertheless. Since 1991 BMW vehicles being taken off the road have been dismantled by independent recycling companies and then reconditioned or recycled in their materials by suppliers, other partners in industry, and BMW itself. These recycling plants incidentally work on behalf of BMW and according to our specifications. In Germany no less than 17 BMW recycling partners have gone into business in the meantime, and we have taken the first preparatory steps with supra-regional system suppliers in order to once and for all close our recycling and waste management cycles. In pilot projects we are even considering to what extent BMW's own dealers may provide additional take-back points for old BMWs.

Assuming global responsibility for our products, we are of course not limiting ourselves to Germany alone. On the contrary, we have already signed on recycling plants in Switzerland and Austria, in France, Great Britain, and the USA. In Switzerland, in fact, we came close to nationwide coverage as early as in 1993 with no less than 21 domestic recycling plants. In France, in turn, BMW and Renault have agreed on close cooperation in the recycling of vehicles, establishing common recycling structures and joining forces in the use of material cycles.

In the USA the initiatives taken by our Company to develop country-specific recycling concepts were lauded in 1992 by the National Recycling Coalition (NRC), awarding us the *Best Recycling Innovation*. Here in Britain BMW received the Environmental Award in 1993 for the establishment of our own recycling centres and for research activities in this area.

Proceeding from many years of studies on the dismantling and recycling of old vehicles, BMW became the first company in 1992 to introduce its own recycling standards. Since then each and every component has been carefully examined at the development phase for its environmental compatibility and its suitability for appropriate recycling in technical, economic, and ecological terms.

To give you just one example of the many details involved in this context and to prove our efforts, I would like to mention only one figure which, to the best of my knowledge, none of our competitors is able even to get close to. The overall recycling ratio of our new BMW 7 Series in terms of weight is a most remarkable 85 per cent, and on the new 5 Series this figure is even a bit higher. Always remember in this context that we are only counting those components and materials which can really be recycled economically.

On the whole, one of the greatest challenges which has always faced us as engineers is to continue improving the automobile in ecological terms, in this way securing its position as an essential source of individual mobility. For there is no doubt as to the benefits offered by, and the need for, the automobile also in future. As I have shown you, we have already made a great deal of progress in this area so far. But to make even more efficient progress in the long term we must pursue an all-round, sensible energy strategy today.

## Alternative Drive Concepts

Considering that fossil energy resources are finite, the only way to solve the conflict we are facing is to introduce regenerating energy step-by-step.

This is why BMW has been working in the area of alternative drive concepts for the automobile for a number of decades now. Our studies have clearly confirmed that hydrogen and electricity offer ideal conditions in the long term.

BMW took up these challenges at a very early point. Just consider the vehicles which accompanied the marathon runners in the 1972 Munich Olympics – BMW 02 Series cars with electric drive. A lot has happened in the meantime and we have pursued our development process into very ambitious and encouraging areas also involving electric drive.

On the other hand we have also strengthened our efforts in using hydrogen energy. The particularly attractive thing about hydrogen is that it may be generated from water by way of solar energy, and oxidates to steam when burnt without releasing any $CO_2$ in the process. A further advantage is that conventional combustion engines may be run without problems on hydrogen. This is why BMW has been working in the area of hydrogen drive since 1978. In the 1980s, BMW built the world's first, and still only, engine test rig for liquid hydrogen. We use this facility to examine and consistently improve the reliability, emission behaviour, performance features, and system costs of the engines being developed.

But on the whole, both electrical and hydrogen energy are not solutions for today or tomorrow. For to offer solutions based on a definite strategy, that is appropriate technical solutions and concepts, we need many years of hard work in order to develop a product oriented to the customer and accepted by society in every respect. I am convinced that in this case we must think in periods of 25 or even 50 years!

Looking at electric drive, just consider the well-known problem of energy storage. The basic problem encountered by the electric car back then and, regrettably, still today, is the limited amount of energy a battery is able to store and provide as drive power. Considering the restraints of electric drive when it comes to the range a car can cover, electric cars will remain niche vehicles in the near future. They will only have a genuine potential where their design criteria are just right for the specific conditions in such a niche market.

Focusing on hydrogen technology, on the other hand, just consider that we still lack suitable solar-driven hydrogen power units today, while at the same time industry and research must still develop the infrastructure for distributing energy and must provide the filling stations required by users.

Although today nobody can say for sure when hydrogen cars will first appear on our roads, BMW's long-term energy strategy focuses on hydrogen and electric energy for motoring. To be able to use such regenerating sources of energy economically in 25 to 50 years, we must develop the foundations required today. In the meantime, our strategy will be completed by providing two interim solutions: First, we are concentrating all our efforts on reducing the energy currently consumed by our vehicles and cutting back the emissions, as I stated before. Second, we are trying to close the gap between today and the more distant future by using natural gas and hybrid drive systems. Both of these concepts are reasonable compromises, both are based on reliable technology, and both can be introduced at relatively short notice.

## Conclusion

In conclusion, allow me to state briefly why we feel that all this is very important for maintaining our individual mobility. Throughout the history of mankind, mobility has been the principle of change, the driving force for evolution. Many people use the mobility ensured by modern technology, and mobility is the very foundation of as well as the prerequisite for the prosperity we enjoy in life today. Without mobility there would not be a functioning economy – it is one of the main cornerstones of our prosperity. And even if some people don't believe it, without mobility there would be no "movement" in the literal sense of the word.

It is above all thanks to the automobile that individual mobility is now a general asset we all enjoy in life. More than 80 per cent of passenger transport is provided by the automobile. The automobile is and will remain the primary means of individual transport, other facilities not being able to provide any capacity worth mentioning. At the same time, however, it is precisely the unique success of the automobile that has inevitably created dramatic consequences. We all know the problem of congested roads, the problem of exhaust emissions in densely populated areas. In conjunction with the considerable increase in international goods transport, our growing leisure-time society will lead to a further increase in transport volume on the road.

All this means that we need new perspectives and approaches in future. We must give up individual interests and focus instead systematically on the overall situation. This applies to us all. All manufacturers are responsible themselves for the improvement of the automobile – I have already told you in detail what we have done. The target, therefore, is to create a product compatible with the environment and the human being in all its features. But this all-inclusive approach is not limited to the automobile alone. Rather, the driver and vehicle, other transport users and providers, our roads and surrounding areas are all becoming parameters of equal significance. Transport today is an overall challenge, the problems and opportunities of each individual means of transport being connected closely with the problems and opportunities of all other types of transport. The motto for the future, therefore, must be co-operation, not confrontation.

In future we will be measured by our success in providing mobility as a whole. This is obviously also a question addressing the responsibility of the carmaker, requiring us to assume responsibility also where we are not directly responsible for the consequences of our actions, but where, through our competence, we are able to provide the answers. Let me give you an example of what I mean in this context by referring to our Traffic Management Project in Munich.

In 1986 we developed our Munich Cooperative Traffic Management System (CMS), taking an entirely new approach by creating a network of aircraft, railways, public short-haul passenger transport, and individual means of transport. This was indeed the first really comprehensive traffic management system ever introduced. People were amazed at the time – how on earth could an automobile manufacturer suggest banning the automobile from the inner city, building P&R terminals, and advocating suburban trains running at more frequent intervals! In the meantime, however, our project has been copied by others.

We have tried to re-define the position the automobile should have in future. The automobile itself must change. The way it is used will change, but it will still continue to offer unbeatable advantages which make us absolutely confident that the philosophy we are pursuing will also secure the future of the automobile.

I do not think that these statements require any further comments. Perhaps I should add, however, that we regard all these challenges of the future as a genuine duty.

First, there is our ecological duty to the environment and society, which I have described in this presentation. There is the economic duty I briefly mentioned at the beginning, calling for a fundamental economic about-face and further development. Bringing this to a point, it means that we have to adjust all structures and processes as quickly as possible to changing conditions in the markets, in this way creating an agile, flexible and global organisation on the basis of environmental awareness.

# Sustainable Product Lifecycles

## Dr Peter R. White

Environmental Science Manager
Procter and Gamble Ltd

## Personal Profile

**Dr Peter White** is Environmental Science Manager at Procter & Gamble's Technical Centre in Newcastle, UK. He joined P&G in 1991 after 14 years of university research and teaching in the Biological and Environmental Sciences.

His responsibilities include the use of lifecycle inventory techniques to help optimise both products and packaging, and the promotion of integrated waste management across Europe.

Along with two P&G colleagues, he has researched and written the recently published book *Integrated Solid Waste Management: A Lifecycle Inventory*. This book combines the two emerging concepts of Lifecycle Inventory and Integrated Waste Management, which will be covered in his presentation.

# Sustainable Product Lifecycles

## Dr Peter R. White

## Introduction

In 1987, the Brundtland Report, *Our Common Future*, introduced the concept of Sustainable Development as development that meets the needs of the present generation without compromising the ability of future generations to meet their own needs (WCED, 1987). Since then there have been many discussions on defining sustainability in practical terms and on how it might be achieved. There is general agreement, however, that there are both environmental and economic elements to Sustainable Development. Economically sustainable development is essential to improve continuously the standard of living of the world's population. Environmental sustainability is required to ensure that this is achieved without causing any environmental deterioration in either this or future generations. One response to this need for both environmental and economic sustainability has been industry's 'more from less' approach (Hindle et al., 1993): the need to provide more value from goods and services from the use of less resources and the production of less wastes and emissions. This paper will show how the 'more from less' approach has led to the introduction of products and packages which provide real environmental benefits, and how it can be used to identify ways to optimise product lifecycles further. If all individual product lifecycles are optimised, however, there will still be solid wastes remaining at the end of each lifecycle that society has to manage. The more from less approach can also be applied to solid waste management.

Sustainable Development requires many partnerships if it is to become established. In particular, shared responsibility is needed between manufacturers of individual products and those authorities that plan and operate society's infrastructure. This paper will show that if designers and manufacturers use a 'more from less' approach to optimise products and packages, whilst waste managers and policy makers use it similarly to optimise waste management systems, the overall result will be more sustainable product lifecycles.

## Overall Environmental Management

Managing the environment is a complicated and multi-faceted operation for both governments and industry (White et al., 1995a). Many different environmental dimensions must be taken into account, especially for a global consumer goods company such as Procter & Gamble. P&G operates in over 140 countries, with a product portfolio of over 300 brands covering several diverse product sectors (laundry and cleaning, personal care, paper, food and beverage), over 120 manufacturing sites and a multitude of suppliers and customers. The interactions of such an organisation with the environment are both numerous and complex, yet they need to be managed. Clearly, no one environmental management tool can be expected to cover all of these interactions. A range of different management tools is required to ensure that all dimensions are addressed and that no environmental concern is ignored. Some of these tools have been derived from the environmental sciences, whilst others are more traditional business management tools (Table 1).

Effective decision-making requires that the information from these many available tools is integrated together. To this end, P&G have constructed an Environmental Management Framework (EMF) (White et al., 1995a) (Table 1), which shows how the various tools can be used, along with experience and judgement, for overall environmental management within a company. Environmentally and economically sustainable environmental management is the overall objective of the framework. To achieve this there are four separate elements:

1 Ensuring human and environmental safety

2 Ensuring regulatory compliance

## Environmental management - an Overall Framework

| Goal | Elements of Goal | Available Tools |
|---|---|---|
| Environmentally and economically sustainable environmental management | **1.** Human and environmental safety | Human Health Risk Assessment (Occupational and domestic exposure)<br>Ecological Risk Assessment (Plant-site and consumer releases) |
| | **2.** Regulatory compliance | Manufacturing site management system auditing.<br>Manufacturing site waste[1] reporting (e.g. SARA, TRI).<br>Material consumption[2] reporting (e.g. Dutch packaging covenant).<br>New chemicals testing and registration.<br>Product and packaging classification and labelling. |
| | **3.** Efficient resource use and waste management | Material consumption[2] monitoring and reduction.<br>Manufacturing site management system auditing.<br>Manufacturing site environmental auditing.<br>Auditing major and new suppliers.<br>Disposal company auditing.<br>Product LCI.<br>Eco-design.<br>Economic analysis. |
| | **4.** Addressing societal concerns (i.e. understand / anticipate & interact) | Understand/Anticipate:<br>• Opinion surveys<br>• Consumer and market research.　• Networking (antenna function).<br>Interact:<br>• Information through presentations and publications to key audiences[3]<br>• Academic, policy and industry work groups (e.g. think tanks, professional bodies, consultants).<br>• Lobbying to influence future policy and regulations.<br>• Corporate reporting　　　• Specific problem solving with others |

**Table 1**

**Notes:** 1. Wastes = emissions to air, water and land. 2. Material consumption = Raw materials and energy consumption for product, packaging and processing. 3. Key audiences = consumers, employees, retirees, opinion leaders and legislators.

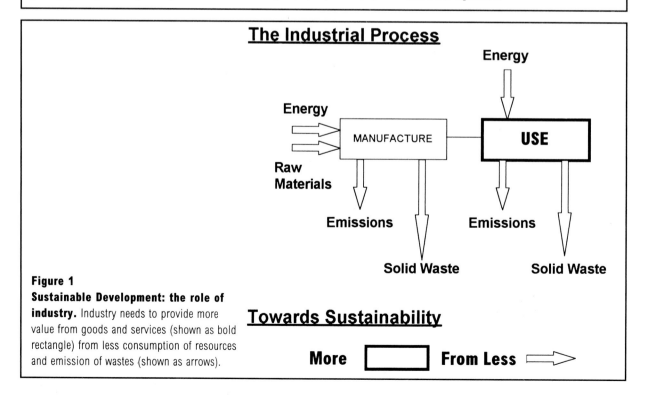

**Figure 1**
**Sustainable Development: the role of industry.** Industry needs to provide more value from goods and services (shown as bold rectangle) from less consumption of resources and emission of wastes (shown as arrows).

**3**  Ensuring efficient resource use and waste management and

**4**  Addressing societal concerns. For each element, several different tools can be of use; conversely, some tools serve more than one element (Table 1).

For a consumer goods company such as P&G, it is of prime importance to ensure that products, packaging and operations are safe, for consumers, production workers and the environment. Safety must be ensured through all stages of a product's manufacture, use and disposal. This requires use of the well-established tools of human and ecological risk assessment (Beck et al., 1981). Secondly, there is the need to ensure compliance with all health and environmental regulations and legislation. Having established human and environmental safety, and regulatory compliance, however, there are further needs for sustainability:- efficient use of resources and management of wastes i.e. more from less.

## More from less – for Products and Packaging

'More from less' requires the efficient use of resources and management of wastes and emissions. This requires a lifecycle approach – looking beyond the traditional boundary of the factory gate to consider all of the stages of a product's lifecycle (Figure 1). For a consumer goods company like P&G, this is especially so. Of the materials that enter P&G's manufacturing plants in Europe, over 98% leaves the plants as products or packaging. Less than 2% is emitted as air-borne, water-borne or solid wastes (P&G, 1994). Monitoring of individual site emissions is important, using site-specific tools such as risk assessment and manufacturing site wastes reporting (Table 1), but it is clearly necessary to look at what happens to the product and its packaging elsewhere in the lifecycle to identify where the most significant environmental improvements can be made.

One of the tools within the overall environmental management framework that can be used to improve resource use and waste management is Lifecycle Inventory (LCI). This involves constructing an inventory of all material and energy inputs and outputs of a product or packaging system, which are associated with providing a particular "service to society". In the case of a product, the service provided would be the function of the product – in the case of a laundry detergent, for example, the washing of clothes a given number of times. In the

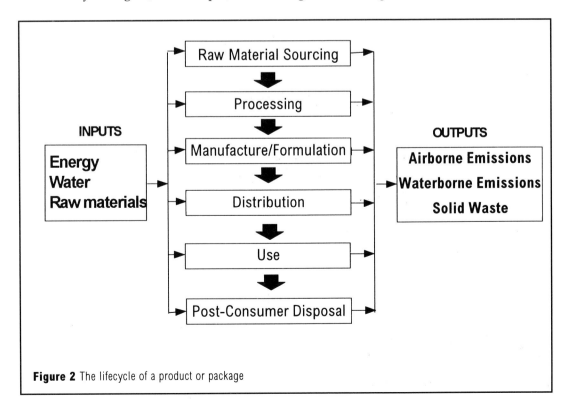

**Figure 2** The lifecycle of a product or package

case of packaging, the service provided would be the safe and intact delivery of a certain amount of contents.

Lifecycle inventory takes a 'cradle to grave' approach, so will include all of the inputs and outputs, from all processes, from all locations in the lifecycle of the product or packaging. All stages of the lifecycle are considered within an LCI for a product or package, including raw material extraction, manufacture, distribution, use and then waste management (see Figure 2). With this broad perspective, LCIs can be used for:

- *Optimisation of the lifecycle*

LCIs can show where the largest environmental burdens occur in the lifecycle, so that these can be addressed, and where possible reduced.

- *Prevention of problem shifting*

As they consider all parts of the lifecycle, LCIs will help ensure that improvements made in one part of a lifecycle do not produce greater deteriorations elsewhere at another stage, time or place in the lifecycle.

- *Allocating all environmental burdens to the particular service provided*

The lifecycle approach is unique in that it looks along the product or package dimension and calculates the overall environmental burdens. This allows the burden to be compared with the value of the service provided, i.e. a value: impact assessment (Hindle et al., 1993).

Unlike its sister tool Lifecycle Assessment (LCA), which attempts to go further and convert the lifecycle inventory into environmental impacts, the methodology for LCI is now established and widely used.

## Using Lifecycle Inventory for Products and Packaging

Many LCI studies have been published, particularly in the field of packaging (see review in White et al., 1993). The value of the lifecycle approach here is that it allows comparison of all the different ways in which products can be packaged. It is possible to compare options that are re-usable, refillable, returnable or recyclable with one way packages that use less material in the first place (i.e. source reduction). This allows some commonly held views such as 'recyclable or re-usable packaging must be better' to be tested. To take one such example, when a plastic pouch was introduced for Ariel Liquid detergent, it was possible to conclude that the pouch, although not readily recyclable, would outperform the more recyclable bottle in terms of energy consumption, air and water emissions and solid waste, since it used much less material in the first instance (White et al., 1993).

P&G have built their own LCI spreadsheet model for packaging (P&G, 1992). Believing that LCI can contribute to more sustainable product lifecycles, P&G made this model freely available on request in 1992. To date, over 500 copies of the spreadsheet have been sent out all over the world. An updated version is currently in progress and will shortly be available.

A similar approach can be used for products. The 'more from less' description of environmentally-improved products was actually first applied to Ariel Ultra in 1989. This laundry product was designed to meet the consumer need of better cleaning performance, whilst it used less product and packaging per wash. This led to significant savings in resource use and emissions all through the lifecycle (see Hindle et al., 1993). When Ariel Future was subsequently launched in 1994, it provided 'even more from even less' – better cleaning again than Ariel Ultra, with even less product and packaging per use.

The lifecycle approach in general, and LCI in particular, therefore allows designers and manufacturers to optimise the use of raw materials and energy, and the management of emissions and wastes across the whole lifecycle of individual products and packages. Successful strategies may include any, or many, of the following: raw material choice, use of recycled materials, light-weighting, product concentration, energy-efficient processing, optimised distribution networks, and design for subsequent recycling or energy recovery. The key objective is to provide the service to society in the most resource-efficient way.

### Gaining Insights from a Lifecycle Approach to Products

Lifecycle thinking can also provide new insights since it broadens the perspective. This can be of strategic importance. Studies of lifecycles for products such as cars have demonstrated that the major environmental burdens occur in the 'use' phase of the lifecycle. Similar insights can be gleaned from other lifecycles, such as for washing clothes. An LCI conducted for P&G on a detergent product in the USA showed that the majority of energy consumption and solid waste generation over the whole lifecycle of washing clothes arose from the heating of the water and the running of the washing machine, rather than the sourcing, making or packing of the detergent. Hot water heating in particular accounted for over 50% of total energy consumption and over 30% of total solid waste generation. This prompts the conclusion that for a detergent producer to reduce the overall environmental burdens associated with the washing of clothes, formulation of a product that performs well at low temperature should offer the greatest potential.

## Sustainable Waste Management

No matter how well optimised each product and package lifecycle may be, however, there will inevitably be some post-use solid waste to be managed. This solid waste is not handled on a product-by-product, or package-by-package basis, however. The management of all the post-use products and packages, i.e. the municipal solid waste (MSW) is usually the responsibility of the local authority or municipality. The development of more sustainable product lifecycles therefore requires a partnership approach involving both the designers and manufacturers of the products and the planners and operators of the waste management systems in which the products and packages will eventually be handled. To this end, P&G has been working with local authorities and organisations such as the European Recovery and Recycling Association (ERRA), the Organic Reclamation and Composting Association (ORCA) and the European Energy from Waste Coalition (EEWC) to promote an integrated and sustainable approach to solid waste management.

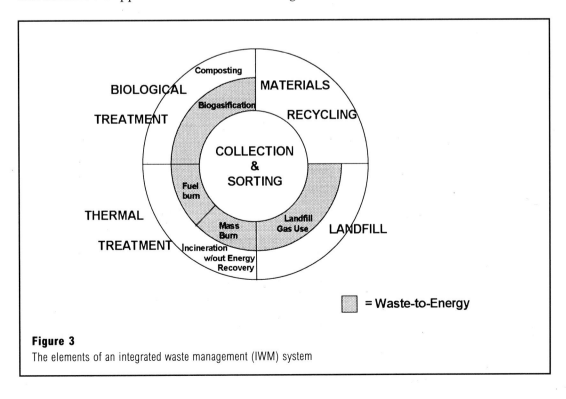

**Figure 3**
The elements of an integrated waste management (IWM) system

## Waste Management Objectives

As with products and packaging, the initial objectives for solid waste management are to ensure human and environmental safety and regulatory compliance (White et al. 1995a). Indeed, historically the objectives of solid waste management have been to dispose of society's waste while safeguarding public health and the health of workers in the waste industry. These still apply, but today there is the additional requirement of efficient use of resources and management of emissions to ensure that solid waste management is sustainable.

## Integrated Waste Management (IWM)

It is becoming generally accepted that no one single treatment method can handle all materials in MSW in an environmentally efficient way. Following a suitable collection system, a range of treatment options will be required including materials recovery, biological treatment (composting and/or biogasification), thermal treatment (burning of refuse-derived fuel (RDF), packaging-derived fuel (PDF) and/or mass-burn incineration) and landfilling (see Figure 3). Together these can form an integrated waste management system.

## Using Lifecycle Inventory for Integrated Waste Management

The same 'more from less' approach used for products can be used to optimise waste management. A waste management system should be able to extract more value from the waste prior to final disposal (as recovered secondary materials, compost and/or energy) from the consumption of less energy and other resources in the process.

Such optimisation of solid waste management requires the ability to compare different integrated systems, to make choices and identify where improvements can be made. Until now, such choices have been based on the so-called hierarchy of waste management options. The exact form of this hierarchy varies but is normally similar to Figure 4.

Relying on the hierarchy of waste management has three major limitations, however. Firstly it has no technical or scientific basis. Secondly, it is of little use in considering combinations of options. It cannot tell us, for example, if a waste management system with materials recycling and landfilling of the residues is better or worse than a system with composting of organics and incineration of the remaining material. While it lists treatment options in a "priority" order, it does not allow comparisons of integrated combinations of options i.e. of

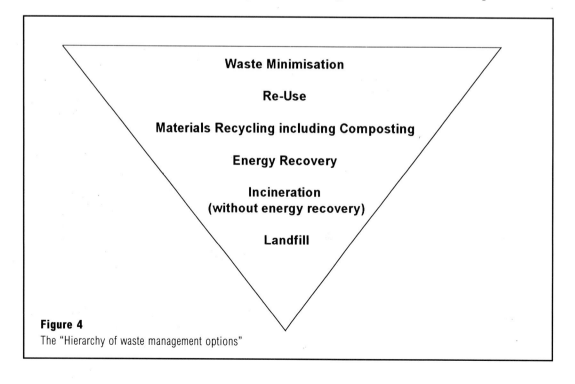

**Figure 4**
The "Hierarchy of waste management options"

different IWM systems. Thirdly, it does not address economic sustainability. Waste management systems need to be affordable to all sectors of the community that they serve, including householders, institutions, local authorities and industry. What is important in optimisation of waste management systems is comparison of overall environmental burdens and overall economic costs. As with products, such overall comparisons can be achieved using the tool of Lifecycle Inventory (LCI).

Some three years ago, P&G began work to apply the technique of LCI to integrated waste management (IWM) systems. This work has now been completed and has been published as a book: *Integrated Solid Waste Management: A Lifecycle Inventory* (White et al. 1995b). The book contains a computer spreadsheet model that allows waste managers and policy makers to carry out an LCI of any solid waste management system, to compare the environmental burdens and overall costs of different options. It can be used to plan future waste management strategies at the level of a town, city, region or country. It can also be used to identify where the major environmental burdens arise from existing systems, so that improvements can be made.

The use of LCI for assessing waste management systems is clearly an idea whose time has come. Both the UK Department of the Environment (DoE, 1995) and the U.S. Environmental Protection Agency (Thorneloe et al., 1995) are currently running similar projects to construct lifecycle inventories for comparing waste management options. Since publication of the P&G book and computer model at the start of this year we have heard from several regional authorities in the UK who are using them to set their future waste management strategies.

## An LCI model for solid waste management

A diagrammatical representation of the inputs, outputs and boundaries of the LCI model for waste management is shown in Figure 5. Full details of the model are given in the book *Integrated Solid Waste Management: A Lifecycle Inventory* (White et al., 1995b). Essentially the model considers the overall energy balance, the amounts of useful products (e.g. compost and recovered materials) and the emissions to air water and land, associated with managing

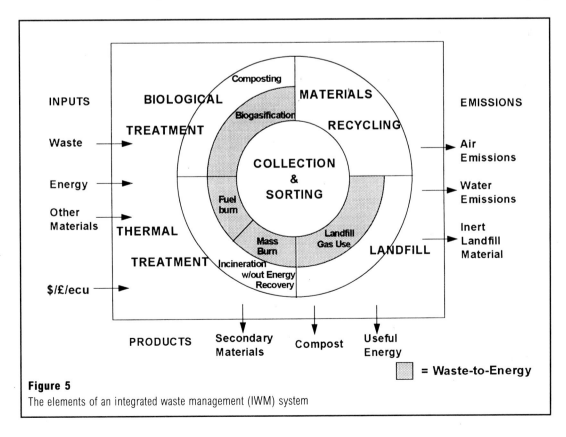

**Figure 5**
The elements of an integrated waste management (IWM) system

the municipal waste of a given area. It covers the lifecycle of waste, 'from dustbin to grave', i.e. from the time the materials are discarded by a householder to the time they become inert landfill material, emissions to air or water, or regain value as useful products. All operations within the waste management system, including the actions of the householder in handling the waste, are included.

## Comparing Solid Waste Management Systems

The LCI model can be used to compare different ways of handling municipal solid waste. It considers the waste generated by an area, and the many ways that this household waste could be managed. It can compare collection from the kerbside, versus bring systems or the use of civic amenity sites; it can involve the use of composting or biogasification for organic materials, the use of a materials recovery facility to separate and process recyclables, the use of thermal treatments such as mass burn incineration, burning refuse-derived fuel (RDF) or packaging-derived fuel (PDF), and the use of landfilling. Any combination of the above treatment methods can be explored in 'what if...?' calculations.

For each of these options, it is possible to calculate the overall energy consumption, and emissions to air, water and land associated with managing the waste. Providing that the priorities for environmental improvements have been decided, e.g. conservation of energy, groundwater protection etc., the preferred waste management option can then be identified. Note that an LCI will not, by itself, identify which option is 'environmentally best' – this will depend on what are considered the most pressing environmental problems in each case.

## Insights from using LCI for Waste Management

As for products and packaging, taking a lifecycle approach to waste can yield interesting and useful insights. As well as the overall comparisons described above, an equally valid use of LCI is to identify where significant environmental burdens exist in the lifecycle of waste.

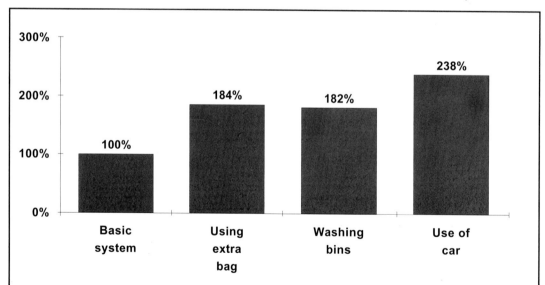

**Figure 6** Effect of householder behaviour on overall energy consumption of solid waste management systems.

**Notes:**
1. Basic system involves commingled collection and landfilling of household waste
2. Extra bag use scenario involves basic system with use of one extra 20g LDPE collection bag per household per waste collection.
3. Bin washing scenario involves basic system plus washing of collection bin with warm water each week.
4. Use of car scenario involves basic system plus one special trip by car per household per week to deliver recyclables to materials banks (2km each way). Assumes 90% petrol:10% diesel cars.
5. Overall energy consumption on basis of thermal energy equivalent. (see White et al., 1995b for further details)

The Challenge for Manufacturing

This will allow improvement efforts to be effectively targeted. Doing this for waste management yields some interesting and perhaps unexpected insights, especially into the overall effects of householder behaviour.

If we consider a basic scenario for UK household waste management, i.e. commingled collection of household waste followed by landfilling, we can see how different actions by the householders will affect the overall energy consumption of the system (Figure 6). Common practices, such as using extra collection bags or washing out bins in warm water, can roughly double the energy consumption of the whole waste management system. Using a car to make special journeys to materials recycling banks can more than double the overall energy consumption. Clearly, anything that is done by individual households will be repeated in every household, so can have a major overall effect. Such unexpected results demonstrate the benefit of a lifecycle approach in showing where significant burdens can occur. In the case of householder behaviour, the above results suggest that any effort and money spent on householder education would be well spent.

## Overall Optimisation of Product Lifecycles

This use of LCI for waste management differs fundamentally from the use of LCI for products or packages. Product LCIs look at the whole lifecycle of individual products from cradle to grave, i.e. a vertical analysis (Figure 7). The LCI for waste management looks at the lifecycle of waste, from the moment materials lose value, to the moment they either regain value (as recovered materials) or become emissions to air, waste or land. Thus this 'horizontal' analysis (Figure 8) looks at part of the individual lifecycles of all the products and packages used by society.

Lifecycle inventory can therefore be applied in two different ways to help develop sustainable product lifecycles. Firstly, LCI can be applied to individual products and packages to optimise their lifecycles from an environmental perspective. These 'vertical' LCIs can be performed by the designers and manufacturers of the products and packages in question. Secondly, LCI can be used to optimise the management of solid waste itself – a 'horizontal' LCI.

Clearly, the two LCI approaches overlap. Part of all product LCIs will be concerned with the time each product or package spends in the waste management system. Conversely, the LCI

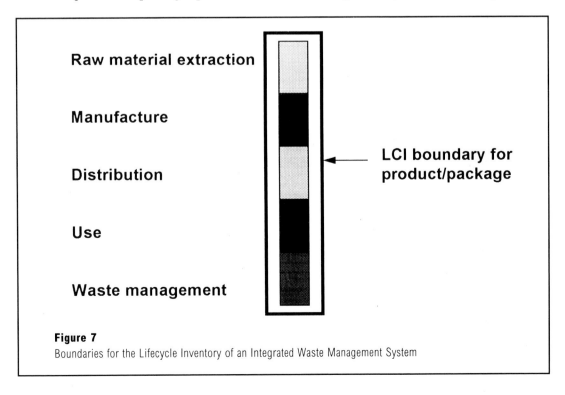

**Figure 7**
Boundaries for the Lifecycle Inventory of an Integrated Waste Management System

**77**

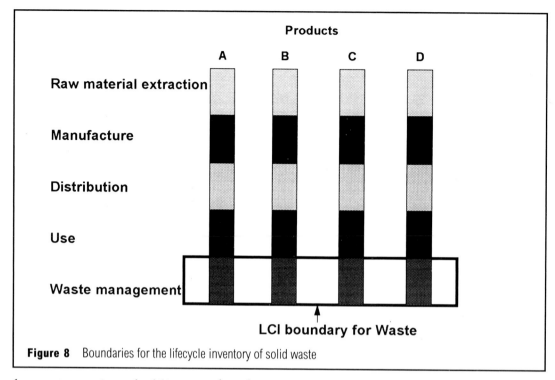

**Figure 8**  Boundaries for the lifecycle inventory of solid waste

for waste consists of adding together the waste management stages of all products and packages. However, they represent two distinct tools for two different user groups. Product LCIs are of use to those who design and manufacture products and packages, and will help them to deliver a service to society in a material- and energy-efficient manner. LCIs for solid waste will be of use to those responsible for the management of solid waste, normally municipalities, regional and national government, to help them optimise the management of the wastes from the communities that they serve.

The two optimisation processes, for products and waste management, will interact. As individual products and packages are optimised, the resultant solid waste entering the waste system will alter. Similarly, as waste management systems are optimised, the waste

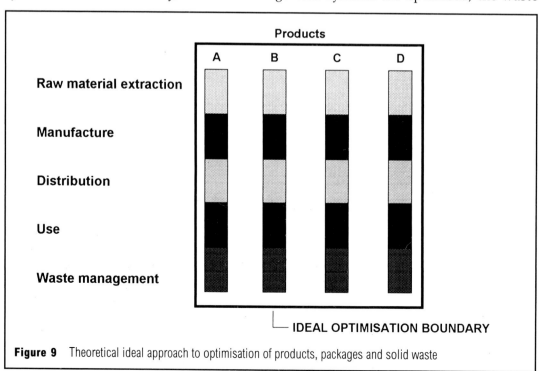

**Figure 9**  Theoretical ideal approach to optimisation of products, packages and solid waste

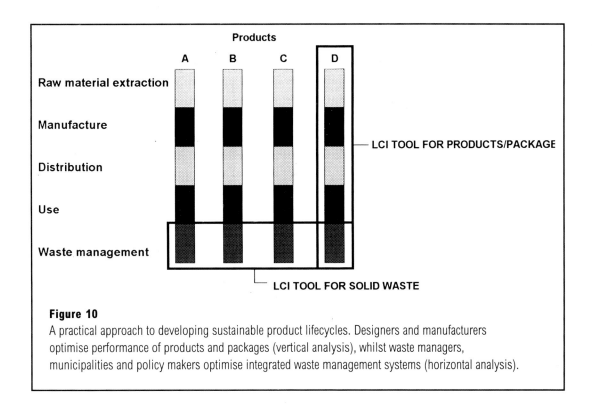

**Figure 10**
A practical approach to developing sustainable product lifecycles. Designers and manufacturers
optimise performance of products and packages (vertical analysis), whilst waste managers,
municipalities and policy makers optimise integrated waste management systems (horizontal analysis).

management stage of every product and package will be altered. Ideally, the answer would
be to include both product and package lifecycles and the waste lifecycle in one system which
could then be optimised. This is the system shown in Figure 9. In practice, however, this
would mean optimising the production and disposal of all products and packages, over all
stages of their lifecycles. In short, the environmental optimisation of industrial society. This
is not feasible, at least not currently! At present, the use of separate 'vertical' and 'horizontal'
analyses, i.e. use of LCIs of products and packages by designers and manufacturers, and the
use of LCI for solid waste by waste managers and waste policy makers, offers the best
potential (Figure 10). This approach of having separate LCI tools which allow the different
actors within the lifecycle of a product to optimise their own operations can be taken further.
It has already been shown that energy consumption can have significant environmental
burdens over a product's lifecycle. Transport can also contribute significantly to overall
lifecycle burdens in some cases. There is thus a need for co-ordinated action by all those actors
involved in the lifecycle of products. If separate LCI tools were used by all actors to optimise
the parts of the lifecycle under their own control, overall this would lead to more sustainable
product lifecycles.

## Conclusions

Lifecycle inventory (LCI) has been shown to be a very useful tool, within the overall
environmental management framework, for ensuring efficient resource use and waste
management. It can be used by a designer or manufacturer on a specific product or package
lifecycle, or to optimise such operations as waste management or energy generation. By taking
a 'cradle to grave' approach, it helps ensure that environmental improvements in one area
are not outweighed by greater problems elsewhere in the lifecycle i.e. that proposed changes
are real environmental improvements. At the end of the day, however, an environmentally-
improved product will only deliver this benefit if it is sold and used in replacement of a
product with a poorer environmental performance. To be sold, products must provide the
value consumers require from them, in terms of both performance and price. Therefore both
economic and environmental factors need to be considered to ensure that a product lifecycle
is sustainable.

## Acknowledgement

The figures in this paper are taken from *Integrated Solid Waste Management: A Lifecycle Inventory*, by P.R. White, M. Franke and P. Hindle. Published by Blackie Academic and Professional (1995) ISBN 0-7514-0046-7.

## References

Beck, L.W., Maki, A.W., Artman, N.R. and Wilson, E.R. 1981. *Outline and criteria for evaluating the safety of new chemicals*. Regulatory Toxicology and Pharmacology 1: 19-58.

Department of the Environment. 1995. *Developing Lifecycle Inventories for Waste Management*. UK Dept of Environment, London. April 1995.

Hindle, P., White, P. and K. Minion. 1993. *Achieving Real Environmental Improvements using Value:Impact Assessment*. Long Range Planning 26: 36-48.

P&G, 1992. *Lifecycle Inventory Spreadsheet for Packaging*. Available from Procter & Gamble, Environmental Quality Department, Newcastle Technical Centre, Whitley Road, Longbenton, Newcastle upon Tyne, NE12 9TS.

P&G, 1994. *Environmental Progress Report*. Available from Procter & Gamble Environmental Quality Department, EuropeanTechnical Centre, 100 Temselaan, Strombeek-Bever, B-1853 Belgium.

Thorneloe, S.A., Friedrich, S., Barlaz, M.A., Ranjithan, R., Weitz, K.A., Kong, E.J., Nishtala, S., Wiles, C., Shepherd, P.B., and Ham, R.K. 1995. *Overview of research to conduct life-cycle study to evaluate alternative strategies for integrated waste management*. Presented at Solid waste management: thermal treatment and waste-to-energy technologies, Washington D.C. April 1995.

WCED, 1987. *Our Common Future*. World Commission on Environment and Development, Oxford University Press, 1987.

White, P.R, De Smet, B., Owens, J.W. and Hindle, P. 1995a. *Environmental Management in an International Consumer Goods Company. Resources, Conservation and Recycling*. (In press)

White, P.R., Franke, M. and Hindle, P. 1995b. *Integrated Solid Waste Management: A Lifecycle Inventory*. 362pp. Blackie Academic and Professional, Glasgow.

White, P., Hindle, P and Dräger,K. 1993. *Lifecycle Assessment of Packaging*. In: *Packaging in the Environment*. (Ed. G. Levy). pp 118-146. Blackie Academic and Professional, Glasgow.

# Session Two
# The Challenge
# for Manufacturing

**Rapporteur**

Professor Roland Clift OBE FEng
Professor of Environmental Technology
University of Surrey

## Personal Profile

**Roland Clift** is Professor of Environmental Technology and Director of the Centre for Environmental Strategy at the University of Surrey. He is Chairman of the Engineering and Physical Sciences Committee of Biotechnology and Biological Sciences Research Council (BBSRC). He is a member of the UK Ecolabelling Board, OST Technology Foresight Panel on Agriculture, Natural Resources and Environment, Management Committee of the DTI/DoE Environmental Best Practice Programme, Science and Engineering Board of Biotechnology and Biological Sciences Research Council and the Technical Opportunities Panel of the Engineering and Physical Research Council.

Professor Clift is also a member of the Comité des Sages – an advisory committee to the EC on application of Life Cycle Assessment to Ecolabelling and the Society of Environmental Toxicology and Chemistry (SETAC).

Professor Ronald Clift is one of the UK's pioneers in the field of Clean Technology, and has led the research initiative in this area supported by three of the national Research Councils. He is one of the few UK academics who are developing the life cycle assessment of products known as 'cradle to grave analysis'. He was responsible for establishing the Centre for Environmental Strategy at the University of Surrey in October 1992 as a focus for this work, and was one of the people instrumental in setting up a unique Postgraduate Engineering Doctorate in Environmental Technology, a joint course between the Universities of Surrey and Brunel, which started in October 1993.

Prior to his appointment as Director of the Centre for Environmental Strategy, Professor Clift was head of the Department of Chemical and Process Engineering at the University of Surrey for 10 years. He is a Fellow of The Royal Academy of Engineering and of the Institute of Chemical Engineers and in the 1994 New Year's Honours was awarded an OBE for his services to science and technology.

# The Challenge for Manufacturing
## Rapporteur's Summary
### Professor Roland Clift OBE FEng

The Chairman asked me, in this Report, to put into focus the lateral issues raised by the speakers. Roughly, this means not just summing up what has been said but trying to put the three contributions, and some from the first session, into a common context. The speakers have all developed their business and management theme, so I will revert to an academic theme and start by defining two important words.

The first of these is paradigm. Sir Ronald Hampel referred to the need for "a paradigm shift in the way the world works". In this context the word derives from the work of the philosopher Thomas Kuhn. A paradigm is essentially a mental map, a way in which to interpret the world and our own actions in it. To put it in Existential terms, a 'paradigm shift' is a change in our sense of being-in-the-world.

One of the characteristics of paradigm shifts is that they happen rather fast. The *Code of Practice on Engineers and the Environment* and the associated *Guidelines on Environmental Issues* illustrate the paradigm shift which is in progress. I chaired the working party which produced these documents for the Engineering Council. The Bishop of Oxford complimented the Guidelines for their clarity. This is due in part to Sara Parkin, who did a great service for the engineering profession by writing much of the Guidelines. She will be a member of the Panel in Session Four. I suggest that it would have been unthinkable, more than about five years ago, for the Engineering Council to encourage these documents or to enlist an 'environmentalist' to help write them. The Guidelines are relatively recent, and are evidently still useful. However, I hope and expect that within a few years they will look antique – left behind as a marker on the road through the paradigm shift.

The other word is sustainability. Unlike 'paradigm', this is a word which is widely used but is very difficult to define. As Dame Rachel Waterhouse said in Session 1, "Sustainable Development can mean pretty much what the speaker wants it to mean". The Brundtland definition, so frequently quoted, is not a definition so much as a declaration of principle – the principle of intergenerational equity, or 'futurity' as it is sometimes termed. The Brundtland declaration also refers to meeting people's needs, and to improving the quality of human life. It is worth noting that it does not explicitly mention financial profit or products. We have the problem of finding an operational definition of 'sustainability' or 'sustainable development'. I will try to help this process.

Figure 1 shows what I regard as the three essential components of sustainability. (Incidentally, I always recommend tri-lobal Venn diagrams like this to my students, as an effective way of giving an impression of Deep Intellect.) The lobe labelled "people" includes the social components of sustainability – including the idea of social equity. Dame Rachel Waterhouse has already referred to this, saying explicitly that you cannot ask everyone in the world to consume less. The "people" lobe also acknowledges the importance of social expectations. Sir Robin Ibbs said, of new refrigerants to replace CFCs: "When it became clear that CFCs with their risk of environmental damage were *no longer acceptable*, it became necessary to develop different refrigerants" (my emphasis). Sir Ronald Hampel introduced ICI's development of KLEA in similar terms. As with so many environmental problems, CFCs were defined to be unacceptable by social processes.

I have put technology and economics together in one lobe as the province of engineering and of business – the theme of this conference and in particular this Session. However, we must not forget "thermodynamics and ecology". I mean here the constraints on our activities imposed by the way the universe works. Other professions have a better grasp of ecology – the behaviour of systems of living organisms – but thermodynamics is surely the province of the engineer. In the Engineering Council Guidelines, we say explicitly that the engineer

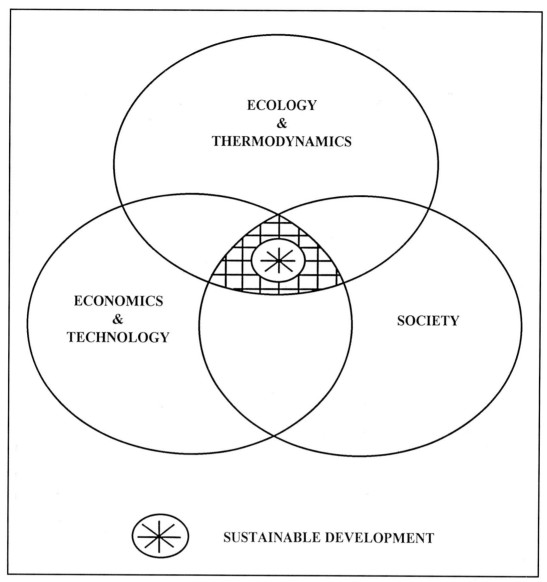

**Figure 1**   The Three Components of Sustainable Development

has a professional responsibility to contribute to public debate. The contribution lies in both 'thermodynamics' and 'technology'. By this I mean that we must point out not only what we can do in practice, now or in the foreseeable future, but also what is absolutely impossible because it is prevented by the laws of thermodynamics. We sometimes have to point out to non-scientists these laws cannot simply be repealed! I think it is consistent with the Brundtland statement to say that Sustainable Development is the area at the centre of the Venn diagram, subject to the constraints arising from all three components. I personally find this helpful – in the search for sustainability, it helps to have some idea where to look! I shall return to this at the end of my summing-up.

Trying to move further towards an operational definition of sustainability, I now introduce Figure 2, which is the best I have been able to do to reduce the human economy to simple thermodynamic terms. Human society – the "people" lobe of the Venn diagram – is sustained by goods and services and gives out emissions, indicated by E on the Figure. Some of these goods and services come from natural systems and agriculture, which also generate their own emissions. In principle the energy for agricultural production should come from the sun. However, there are also large inputs of non-renewable resources – including fossil energy – into agriculture, and this is something which has to be addressed in a sustainable future.

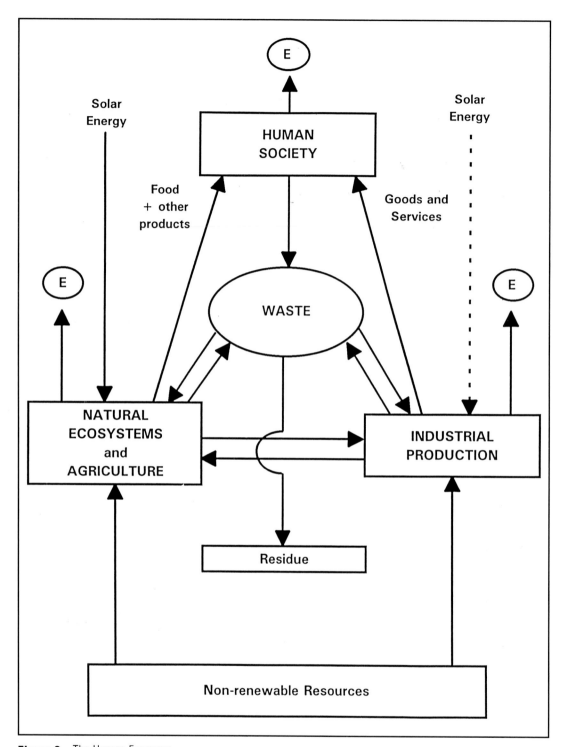

**Figure 2** The Human Economy

Human society also draws goods and services from industrial production. Here, the proportion of energy from renewable sources, ultimately deriving from solar energy, is small: the industrial revolution and subsequent technologies have been powered mainly by fossil energy. As Dr Ziebart pointed out in this session, fossil energy is non-renewable and therefore is not sustainable. Because we cannot beat the thermodynamic constraint, sustainable development has to proceed eventually without non-renewable resources. This means living on "current account" solar energy. It also means shifting emphasis from industrial towards agricultural production. We have seen examples of this aspect of the paradigm shift in this Conference. BMW is looking at hydrogen as a transport fuel, produced by conversion of solar energy. ICI is involved in the development of biosynthetic feedstocks.

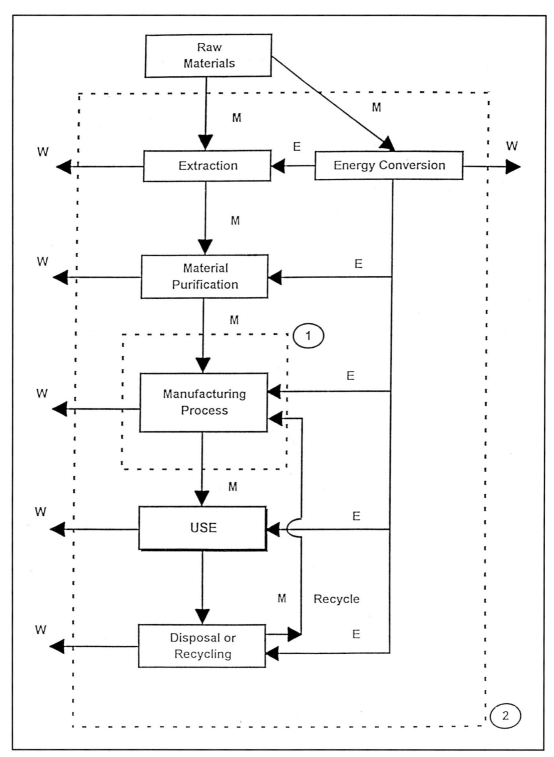

**Figure 3** Environmental System Analysis – 1. Plant, Process or Factory; 2. Life Cycle

The next thing to be pointed out is that the earth is, in thermodynamic terms, a closed system – matter neither leaves nor enters. Therefore the waste produced by human society, agriculture and industrial production remains within the system, as shown in Figure 2. (Actually this is also true of dispersed emissions, but including this makes Figure 2 too complicated and obscures the central points.) We therefore have to think about the best use of waste. This is where Dr White's contribution fits in. Sustainable Development must treat waste as an actual or potential asset. 'Sustainable waste management' then ceases to be a contradiction in terms, and represents another component of the paradigm shift. Emissions and unsusable wastes are evidence of mis-used resources. The paradigm has shifted from "dilute-and-disperse", through pollution abatement, to clean technology.

All the speakers in this Session, and many of those in Session One, referred to Sustainable Development as "more from less". More of what? If we take the Brundtland statement seriously, this means more satisfaction of human needs and better quality of life, not necessarily more profit or more products – in other words, more human benefit. This leads naturally into Life Cycle Assessment, which deliberately concentrates on benefit or function rather than product. As an example from this Session, Dr Ziebart described the business of BMW as providing mobility, rather than selling cars.

I find it interesting that all the contributions in this Session, and most of the contributions to this Conference, embody life cycle thinking, if not formal Life Cycle Assessment. This is further evidence of the paradigm shift we are living through. A few years ago, particularly in Britain, Life Cycle methodologies were being advocated only by a few enthusiasts like Peter White and myself. Now life cycle thinking is a routine part of responsible environmental performance.

Figure 3 illustrates the difference between Life Cycle Assessment and conventional environmental management. Before the paradigm shift got under way, we thought of environmental management as limiting wastes and emissions – "W" in Figure 3 – from a process or factory. In other words, we concentrated on System 1 in Figure 3. Life Cycle Assessment asks where the material and energy flows come from, where they go to, and what wastes and emissions arise along the way. In other words, it enlarges the system to everything within boundary 2 in Figure 3. It also concentrates not on the product but on its use – on the human benefit which it delivers.

As Peter White pointed out, Life Cycle Inventory is the process of identifying and trying to quantify all the flows across system boundary 2. My experience supports his view that the information obtained in this way is always useful, frequently gives surprising insights, and may be sufficient to support strategic decisions. His paper gives a good example of such a surprising insight: well-meaning individual actions can worsen, and sometimes greatly magnify, the environmental impacts of waste management. This is an example of 'profligate environmentalism': doing something which makes you feel virtuous but is actually environmentally damaging.

Life Cycle thinking helps to avoid another form of profligate environmentalism: "reducing waste" by transferring it somewhere else in the Life Cycle. This links back to our duty, as engineers, to ensure that public debate recognises the constraints of thermodynamics. Some lobby groups advocate the "waste-free factory" or "pollution-free factory", but we know that this is thermodynamically impossible. A Life Cycle Inventory can help to expose the fallacy. Dr Elliott, in Session 3 of this Conference, gives us an example by exploding the myth of the "pollution-free vehicle". Several studies have shown that tightening emission standards on one part of the Life Cycle (typically the manufacturing plant or process) can increase overall emissions, usually by increasing energy consumption in manufacturing. I wonder whether our new Environment Agency will recognise this part of the paradigm shift.

As Sir Ronald Hampel said, the paradigm shift is essential. Dame Rachel Waterhouse pointed out that the shift has to go beyond minor changes which have no real effect on lifestyles, to the deeper changes which will be needed if we are serious about sustainable development. I agree with Sir Ronald Hampel that this will not be brought about solely by regulation. So what other changes can we foresee?

Most of our speakers have referred to "closing the cycle" of material use in some way. This needs new commercial and professional relationships. Dr White referred to the interactions between life cycle designers and waste managers. Sir Ronald referred to new relationships between customers and suppliers. Dr Ziebart described the new relationship between BMW and its distributors. Sir Ronald spoke of ICI's commitment to Product Stewardship, while Dr Ziebart outlined BMW's plans for taking back used cars. If the manufacturer supplies the product for a payment, and takes it back once the user has finished with it, the distinction between selling and leasing becomes decidedly fuzzy. Again, the emphasis is on benefit rather than product, leading to leasing as the ultimate form of product stewardship. The concept brings with it the new design principles articulated by Glyn England in the discussion: life-extension, re-use of components, and separation of materials.

The Brundtland statement emphasises satisfying needs. This points to another aspect of the paradigm shift: identifying real needs, not creating false needs. BMW recognises that its business is to satisfy the need for mobility. Dr Ziebart also gave us figures for BMW's improvements in the fuel efficiency of its 200 bhp engine. I cannot avoid asking whether the need for mobility has to be satisfied by a four-seater car with a 200 brake horse power engine.

However, I liked Dr Ziebart's description of how BMW encourages its employees to "lead from the front" by adopting less environmentally-damaging lifestyles. I asked him the testing question. Yes, they do subsidise transport to encourage their staff not to come to work in their own cars.

I can now try to sum up the features of the paradigm shift, exemplified by the contributions here. Figure 1 helps. The market economy, with which we are all familiar, corresponds to the "economics and technology" lobe. The idea of the social market economy is currently vilified in this country but is familiar enough in continental Europe. It corresponds essentially to the overlap of "economics and technology" with "people". In Northern Europe, the discussion is now around the concept of the ecological social market economy. In terms of Figure 1, this corresponds to where all three lobes overlap. In my terms, this should be the place to look for sustainable development.

**Dr Brian Eyre FEng** AEA Technology

We have had a lot of discussion this afternoon about product life cycles. I want to address the point about liability management related to the industrial process. We have all seen the industrial wastelands that have been left when plants have been closed down. For example, coalmines and even the major engineering industries. Most recently this issue was highlighted by the Brent Spar incident. What do we do about offshore rigs, what do we do about nuclear plants when they finish their lives? Sir Ronald Hampel talked about management systems. I will address my question first to him, though I think that it relates to all three speakers. What is your company's policy when a plant that has been a profit-earning asset comes to the end of its life and becomes a potential liability. Do you have a strategy for dealing with this in your company?

**Sir Ronald Hampel**

We have a policy which accepts responsibility for all our sites, all over the world. The way in which we treat each individual site depends on how long it has been there, what it is making, and so on. At one extreme there are the old sites which have been in the company's hands or its predecessors for many years. While we don't actually know what happened on those sites in bygone days, we have carried out assessments in recent times. Society at the moment accepts two things, one is that so long as there are current operations at the site and so long as there is no seepage in one form or another there isn't an issue. This is simplistic but true. On the other hand, there are modern sites built to modern standards and where we have a full record of activities. However, the moment you shut the site then society gets excited and the difference to me is somewhat tenuous. I therefore, and indeed my company, take the view that we have to manage all our sites on an ongoing basis. There comes a point in some industries where the ability of the corporate entity to deal with that issue is beyond it, but that has not yet been the case in the chemical industry. So I believe my answer is satisfactory from my industry's point of view but possibly not from yours.

**Dr Brian Eyre**

In my experience, the management skills, the management priorities, in dealing with situations where a plant becomes a liability are rather different to those when you are actually managing it as an asset, and can contribute a problem to the company.

**Sir Ronald Hampel**

You have got to deal with it in two separate issues. Any management that over the last 20 years has not actually addressed the issue that some day in the future a particular site may not be an industrial site, has not been living in today's world. The issues for us are primarily associated with sites that have been there for a long time and where the techniques of measurement historically were not available to measure what was going on. The reason that standards today are harsher on all of us is partly that measurement has become possible, quite apart from understanding the implications. So, for me, if you start from here the answer's easy. You don't put up a site anywhere in the world today without considering the total long term implications of the impact of that site on the total environment. What you are addressing is history. I accept, and I will for so long as we are commercially viable, that we have a responsibility to deal with our own sites. Let me give you an example which shows how society operates. About two years ago, one afternoon our share price dropped by about four per cent. We are used to fluctuations nowadays but this was slightly surprising. So we enquired as to what was going on. It took quite some time to discover that an agency in the United States had issued a suit against eight companies, to restore San Francisco Bay to the state it was in 1935. One of those companies had been owned in the past by a company we later acquired. Now I don't know what this means, and neither did anyone else, but they actually addressed it to the eight companies who had sites around the Bay over the last hundred years. The commercial implication of that, quite apart from the scientific justification, was horrendous and fortunately it was thrown out. The problem is to deal with it in a rational way. I've given you a rational answer. You, in your industry above all else, recognise that you are not dealing with rationality, you are dealing frequently with emotion. But I don't change my position as a result of that.

### Dr Peter White

I'm not sure I can add anything after that comprehensive answer. I can confirm that, on new sites, you can take the whole life cycle of the site into account. Existing sites have to be monitored, audited and managed. One thing that perhaps should be borne in mind is that consumer goods companies are essentially mixers and packers. We take ingredients and we formulate to make products, then pack them and sell them, so the issue of contaminated land does not tend to be a great issue for us. But if we need to close sites then they are closed so that they are fit for subsequent use.

### Stuart Miller CBE FEng Chairman

I think there is quite a problem of contaminated land in Germany, Dr Ziebart. Perhaps not specifically in BMW's ownership but more generally.

### Dr Wolfgang Ziebart

This has not been an issue for us until about five years ago. We have very severe laws in Germany. However, when we joined with East Germany this became a severe problem. As you know, in East Germany everything was just dumped into the soil. Today we know that all those plants that we have there have moved from an asset to a liability and it will cost us an enormous amount of money to make the land usable again.

### Chairman

The summing up of that is that there is a whole range of circumstances affecting the liability which a company has and Dr Eyre's organisation represents one extreme.

### William Turner Nuclear Electric plc

Dr White mentioned that cost was a major driver in waste management. Does he see a role for environmental damage costing in bringing life cycle analysis more into the decision making process?

### Dr Peter White

I can see that cost is a driver. As more costs are added in – environmental reparation costs – remediation costs, that will affect the overall economics. I don't see that including them will drive the use of life cycle techniques, certainly not on the environmental side. It is tempting to produce some sort of overall tool that takes into account economics, environment and social issues, but I think that if ever anybody got round to creating such a life cycle tool it would be so heavy, cumbersome and so complicated it would never get used. What we do is to separate the environmental side and use life cycle inventory, as opposed to the full life cycle assessment, because we don't think that full assessment methodology has developed yet. Cost information will be included, and other influences, social, and so on, will be put into the decision making process, but I don't think that converting everything into cost is going to make people make more use of life cycle analysis. I would rather keep those three aspects, cost, environment and social, separate and then make a decision, rather than create some huge expert system that does all the deciding for you.

### Professor Roland Clift OBE FEng

I'm not sure if what you are hinting at is the use of what is sometimes called internalising the externalities, which is the notion that you can put a financial figure on all environmental impacts. I happen to be one of the people who think that notion is fundamentally flawed. I think there is a reason why it has become popular, however. It actually relates back to something that was said this morning. If you can convince a decision maker that you have got a simple metric which enables him to weigh off polar bears against buttercups he is going to use it because he feels more comfortable. Actually, it's just another way of hiding serious issues which have to be decided. I agree very much with Peter White, life cycle inventory is a powerful tool. The further you take it beyond that, the shakier it gets and I would be against taking it all the way and putting financial values on environmental impacts, because I think that obscures the real decisions which are being made.

### Sir Ronald Hampel

In practical terms though, the cost of dealing with the environment is now part of every project in one way or another. Our industry, and I'm not talking now specifically about one company, has many plants where you can either spend a sizeable sum of money to bring them up to date with environmental requirements, or shut them down. This is the reality. But I agree that you can get too complex and it leads you off the right track.

### Sara Parkin Forum for the Future

We've heard reference several times to the opportunities that there are for engineering in the environment. The OECD study suggested that there was a very large market here and that it was set to grow by over 5 per cent in the coming years. I have just read a study which was produced in Holland which looked at which countries were actually taking a lead in capturing a larger share of this market, and the strongest correlation they found was the presence of Green Party people in parliament. I would be very interested to hear from our German contributor, and also from our British industrialists, whether there is a real difference in what they can do to take advantage of all the exciting possibilities for environmental technology because of the positions that governments take, the way they legislate and so on.

### Dr Wolfgang Ziebart

Can I change your question a little. You are asking whether we are mainly driven by laws or mainly driven by customer demand. Can we change the question in that way?

### Sara Parkin

It's a combination of the two, it's the climate that is created.

### Dr Wolfgang Ziebart

In our situation, we are selling cars to the very high end of the market, powerful large cars, and those cars are perceived to be environmentally unfriendly. That is the main reason why we have to be far ahead of the competition and the standards and to really care for that type of image. That is our main driving force, not the Greens or the share that they have in parliament, not the standards and the laws. Our special position in the market is our main driving force.

### Sir Ronald Hampel

Any industrialist who pretends that he is not affected by public pressure, wherever it comes from, is kidding himself and whoever he says it to. But like all these things it's a balance.

I think that the real responsibility of management in terms of the long term future of its own corporate entity is to anticipate the opportunities in the future. The opportunities come, to some extent, by anticipating the future pressures.

Lord Tombs asked me earlier about the degree to which we had been driven by Government and regulation in developing new products. I wish it was always like that. One of the characteristics of the chemical industry has been that it has been saved by the inventiveness of its chemists. This inventiveness has recovered positions which had been lost either through poor management or through competition developing elsewhere. We don't see the same opportunity over the next twenty five years of being saved by that route. Yes, there will be new products and new processes but they will tend to be replacements, not brand new, and the degree to which you can exploit them will be dependent on the environment into which you present them. Clearly this area is one of the most exciting. I believe that the companies that will be successful look at this as an opportunity rather than as a threat, and they direct their forward strategic thinking down avenues within which they can make real progress by taking advantage of these shifts, either in knowledge or in emotion. You have to recognise that emotion is part of this. If I really want to tease my oil company friends I say to them "What thinking have you done about the time when petrol disappears from this globe and about the impact that is going to have on your industry?" – clearly our questioner is down that track.

### Chairman

Dr White mentioned working in Brussels. There may be some European Union comment that you would like to make.

### Dr Peter White

I'm not qualified to speak on behalf of the European Union I'm afraid, but I would like to say, regarding a correlation between environmental technology and Green politicians, that the problem with correlations is that they can be false correlations. The question could be asked "Why do they have Green politicians in these countries?" They are there because the voters, the consumers, obviously want them and therefore there is the pull from consumer need. There are two aspects, the need which is to be met by these technologies, as well as the pressure from the Green legislators. Our company has as its mission to fulfill the needs of the world's consumers, and in some countries environmental compatibility is one of those consumer needs. People will buy products because of their environmental performance. But that doesn't go for every country. The needs of the world's consumers are not uniform. They vary very widely.

### Chris Tuppen BT

I would like to return to the question of 'more from less'. Perhaps first to offer an example from industry. In 1915 it took 18 kilograms of copper per kilometre of cable to make a telephone call. Today it takes 0.001 grammes of glass per kilometre of cable to make the same telephone call. If I look at the projections of growth in global economies and growth of populations, I have heard a number of commentators relate Sustainable Development to a reduction in whole-life, non- renewable resources per unit of product by a factor of 10. I would be interested to know if the panel shares that point of view and, if so, when their respective industries might achieve it.

### Dr Peter White

That extrapolation can be little more than a guess. The 'more from less' idea, taken to extreme, becomes 'more from even less'. You can improve continuously as we heard from Sir Ronald. Total quality theory says that you continuously improve by making small improvements with present technology and then at some point you have Professor Clift's paradigm shift, you have the quantum leap and you have a new invention. Using your example, you go from less copper to even less copper until someone says "Hey, fibreoptics". And then you'll get thinner fibreoptics and better fibreoptics, and then someone will say "We don't need fibreoptics anymore, we have X", and if I knew what X was I'd be making it now. So 'more from less' is a working strategy, but at some point there will be a quantum shift into something different which provides equal value, the same usefulness but consumes less. What we are essentially doing is replacing materials and energy by intelligence, by technology and knowledge. Less material goes into it, but a lot more thought. The extrapolation you mention is someone's guess. Someone else will come up with a different guess. I couldn't tell you how accurate it's going to be.

### Dr Wolfgang Ziebart

I cannot comment on the tenfold improvement, but, referring to the car, our main problem is that in the less developed countries there is a huge demand for transportation. Globally speaking, this will cause the main problem in the next decade, to cater for all the transportation in those countries.

### Sir Ronald Hampel

I can only put Peter White's point in a slightly different way. We talk about Sustainable Development today based on our current knowledge of current processes and current demands of society. The only thing we can be certain of is that it will be totally different 10 years from now and the things that will drive us will be different. If you are an optimist, and I am, I believe many of these problems will disappear through scientific development in the broadest sense of the word. It's not an argument for not managing what we are seeking to manage today, because the time scale will be different from that which I have just postulated. At the end of the day, it is an essential discipline that we maintain of the standards we set for ourselves. I do believe however that over time things will change quite dramatically and your own illustration is a very good one.

### Sir William Barlow FEng

First I have a comment then a question. If Sara Parkin is right that where there are Green politicians there seems to have been more progress on this whole subject, and if, Dr White's answer is that there must be consumer demand that is not satisfied and therefore causes there to be Green politicians, then it would follow that in this country, because we haven't got any, consumer demand is well satisfied. We must be doing the right things on sustainable development. That isn't right either, it isn't like that. I really don't know what the answer is on this political thing.

I want to ask a question of Dr Ziebart which follows on from "more from less". The car industry has been very quick to form public opinion on certain aspects of car design in recent years. For example, there has been a lot of interest aroused on emissions and when you advertise your cars you talk about their emissions performance and that has led to the catalytic converter legislation. The same has happened on safety. Some car advertisements now, the Volvo is a particular example, make a great play about the safety of their body shells. Airbags are now pretty well standard, so public opinion has been formed rapidly, but the one thing you don't seem to go for is weight. You mentioned in your lecture what you have done about some aspects of the BMW. You have looked at aluminium suspension. But both in the case of the 5 series and the 3 series you have retained a steel body shell. You have optimised its design to improve its strength/weight ratio but nevertheless you are using materials that are fundamentally heavy unlike, say, the aircraft industry. It's not only BMW. If you look at the buses trundling around London, the old double decker RM series weighs 7.7 tons. Its modern replacement weighs 9.8 tons and the single decker weighs 10.5 tons. We've got transport everywhere that seems to me to weigh about 25% more than it needs to, with all the knock on effects on energy. I ask you, as a designer and manufacturer, why is it that the car industry has not yet got at this weight problem, with the exception of Audi with the A8?

## Dr Wolfgang Ziebart

Actually, I spent my first two years at BMW in charge of the weight reduction programme for the company. I too regret that the customer is not conscious about weight. In Germany, weight is seen as something which has a certain value that corresponds to what you have paid, and if you have a heavy car it is a safe car. Nobody says this but everybody feels that it is the case. I must admit, as I mentioned in my presentation, that we have achieved much more progress in exhaust and safety improvement than we have in weight. The main reason for that is that the whole reduction in weight which we have gained has been used up in improvements in safety, strengthening the body shell for example, and in comfort such as sound deadening material. If you have electric windows they are heavier than manually operated. That is the reason why with the introduction of the latest models we were just able to maintain the weight, so every improvement in the car's structure allowed us to make additions to the specification.

THE ROYAL ACADEMY OF ENGINEERING

# Engineering for Sustainable Development

## SESSION THREE

### The Challenge for Transport

**Chairman** Professor Tony Ridley CBE FEng
**Rapporteur** Alec Silverleaf CB FEng

**Transport from Buchanan
to Sustainability and Telematics**
Professor Peter Hills OBE

**System Problems and Incremental Solutions:
Can the Foresight exercise help?**
Dr Christopher Elliott

**The Realities of Managing
Car Dependence**
David Worskett FIHT

## Session Three
## The Challenge
## for Transport

### Chairman

Professor Tony Ridley CBE FEng
Department of Civil Engineering
Imperial College

## Introduction

Over a number of years, and increasingly during the 1990s, transport has been seen as imposing heavy environmental problems on Society. The public notices this most immediately in the form of traffic congestion. Yet there is increasing concern about noise, visual intrusion and – most powerfully – air pollution with rather vaguer worries about 'the hole in the ozone layer' and global warming. The extent of the problems are not yet well understood and even the Royal Commission on Environmental Pollution report on *Transport and the Environment* did not find universal acceptance.

One of the difficulties is that the provision of good transport, of free movement, is seen by many as the right of the citizen. Furthermore, the fact that economic growth seems to be dependent on efficient transport leads us to down play environmental problems, particularly when the individual finds it hard to believe that he/she is imposing more than minimal damage. In the transport session of this conference we seek to examine the immense complexity of the issues involved – through addresses by a Transport Engineer, a Systems Engineer and a representative of the users. While no sensible action is possible without understanding and analysis of the problems, our focus will be on what engineers can do to tackle transport engineering for sustainable development.

## Personal Profile

**Professor Tony Ridley** holds the Chair in Transport Engineering in the Department of Civil Engineering at Imperial College, where his chair is sponsored by the Rees Jeffreys Road Fund. Until recently he was also the Director of the University of London Centre for Transport Studies.

He joined the Board of Eurotunnel as a non-Executive Member in 1987 and was Managing Director of the project for two years. Previously he was eight years with London Transport and was Chairman and Chief Executive of London Underground Limited. He was Managing Director of the Hong Kong Mass Transit Railway Corporation from 1975-1980 and was the first Director of the Tyne and Wear Passenger Transport Executive from 1969-1975.

Professor Ridley holds a Doctorate in Transportation Engineering from the University of California as well as civil engineering degrees from the University of Newcastle Upon Tyne and Northwestern University. He attended the Senior Executive Program at Stanford Business School in 1980.

Professor Ridley is President of the Institution of Civil Engineers and a Fellow of the Chartered Institute of Transport (for several years he was Chairman of its Transport Policy Committee). He is a former President of the Light Rail Transit Association and has been active in the International Union of Public Transport. He is a member of the Research Council of the European Centre for Infrastructure Studies and represents The Royal Academy of Engineering in a programme of work on Transport by the European Council of Applied Sciences and Engineering (Euro-CASE).

# Transport from Buchanan to Sustainability and Telematics

## Professor Peter Hills OBE

Professor of Transport Engineering and Director of the Transport Operations Research Group, University of Newcastle Upon Tyne

## Personal Profile

**Professor Peter Hills** began his professional career as a member of the Working Group on the Buchanan Report *Traffic in Towns*. After leaving the (then) Ministry of Transport, he spent nine years as a Lecturer at Imperial College, London, and was engaged in numerous consulting studies. In 1972, he was appointed Assistant Director of Research at Leeds University in the newly formed Institute for Transport Studies.

In 1977, he moved to Newcastle University to take up his present post, where he is responsible for a large research group with about 10 current projects in the fields of Urban Traffic Control, Public Transport Operations, Freight Movement, Traffic Safety and Road Traffic Informatics. Besides *Traffic in Towns*, he is co-author of the book *Motorways in London* and many other publications in the transport field. Over the period 1970-81, he was Associate Editor of the international quarterly journal *Transportation*. Over the period 1983-86, he directed the team which produced *Roads and Traffic in Urban Areas* for the Institution of Highways and Transportation. This was published jointly with the DTp in October 1987. From 1985 to 1989, he was appointed by the Secretary of State for Transport as a 'Visitor' to the TRRL (Safety and Transportation Group).

In 1988, he formed a consortium of European partners (including Newcastle University/Polytechnic, Philips UK and Sweden, Philips Components in Germany, CSEE in France and EID in Portugal) to bid for an EC research contract through the DRIVE programme. The bid was successful and led to the PAMELA project in DRIVE I. The consortium is now enlarged in DRIVE II and is developing an automatic two-way communications system between moving vehicles and the roadside, using microwave communications and smartcard technology (the ADEPT project). This project, coordinated from Newcastle, will have many important European-wide applications in (for example) automated toll collection, fleet control, route guidance, online parking information and road use pricing.

In July 1992 he was inaugurated as the President of the Institution of Highways and Transportation for the year 1992/93. He was invited by the EC to act as a Technical Auditor for the DRIVE programme in October 1990 and again in 1991. He also accepted invitations by the UK Department of Transport to serve as a member of SACTRA (Standing Advisory Committee on Trunk Road Appraisal) in 1989 and to act as Special Advisor on research into network management (in 1992). Also for the DoT, he is a member of the Advisory Group on the revision of the National Road Traffic Forecasts (NRTF).

# Transport from Buchanan to Sustainability and Telematics

### Professor Peter Hills OBE

## Introduction

When I was invited to give this paper and Tony Ridley (with his usual enthusiasm) urged on me this title *Transport from Buchanan to Sustainability and Telematics*, I had a uneasy feeling that 30 minutes would not be long enough to do justice to such a task. But I will try. My main qualification for attempting this is that it spans my working life to date – well Buchanan and Telematics certainly do, "sustainability" I am less certain about! Indeed, I first became aware at an early stage in my professional career – having just graduated with an M.Sc. in Highway and Traffic Engineering from Birmingham University – of the scope and complexity of urban transport problems, as a member (albeit very junior) of the so-called Urban Roads Study Group in the (then) Ministry of Transport. Rt Hon Ernest Marples MP had set up this Working Group in 1961, charged with the task of producing what became the Buchanan Report *Traffic in Towns*, published in November 1963. During the ensuing 32 years, the scope has widened and the complexity has increased substantially. Nevertheless, in several key respects, what was envisaged and speculated upon in that report has come about. Inevitably, though, much else has unfolded in ways that the Buchanan Report team could not have foreseen.

In this presentation, I will be able to enjoy the luxury of hindsight, looking back over three decades during which the average per capita income in this country has risen 75% in real terms, car ownership has increased more than two and a half times and the total amount of personal travel has grown almost threefold. Thus, in the realms of prediction, the Buchanan Report certainly did not exaggerate the scale of future increases in urban traffic, although it foresaw a more rapid onset, mainly due to the buoyant forecasts of both population and economic growth that were current in the 1960s. Nor was the Report misguided in characterising the nature of the problem, in terms of the head-on clash between demands for vehicle use and the resulting impacts on the environment. The environmental aspects of concern at that time were, almost without exception, local in their impact and related mainly to the physical attributes of traffic flow. True, more recent concerns centre on the wider public health and even global impacts, which were not foreseen, but the fact is Buchanan anticipated the Environmental Debate in urban transport by almost 20 years.

Over the three decades of economic growth (checked only by the recession in the early 1990s) and periodic boosts of expansion and redevelopment, the overall improvement to the physical fabric of urban areas has been considerable. As part of this process, many of the principles enunciated in the Buchanan Report were adopted, at least partially, and influenced, sometimes in rather watered down form, the policies that many local authorities subsequently pursued. Several of these principles, however, have **not** stood the test of time: notably the idea of vertical segregation, of pedestrian "decks" embodied in a new traffic architecture, which perished in the 1970s as part of a general rejection of plans for comprehensive redevelopment in the central and inner areas of towns and cities. The rejection, in large cities at least, of building major networks of high capacity roads began somewhat later, in the 1980s – although the seeds were sown in the outcome of the Greater London Development Plan in 1975-76 – and has acquired momentum ever since.

Some of the other principles **have** stood the test of time. These include the notion of 'environmental capacity', by defining the limit of traffic volumes and speeds that are acceptable in residential areas, with what Buchanan called "Environmental Traffic Management" being given new life through the traffic calming initiatives of the 1990s.

Pedestrianisation of old city centres and major shopping streets has gradually gained acceptance and is no longer stubbornly resisted by traders faced, as they are, by vigorous out-of-town competition. The implications of town centres fighting back as viable commercial and retail centres have not really been thought through in the current debate. The main unresolved issue turns on the provision (or otherwise) of large amounts of cheap (or even free) parking for shoppers close to central areas and of new urban roads to serve them. True, the Buchanan principles that planning and transport policies must interact and that traffic is a function of land use activity are being rehabilitated handsomely by this new planning guidance, after more than 15 years in abeyance, but trying to apply them without resort to comprehensive redevelopment and major road building raises the same issue confronted by *Traffic in Towns* – namely the inevitability of traffic restraint.

## The Inevitablility of Traffic Restraint

The theory behind the Leeds case study in the Buchanan Report pointed to a city size of only about 150,000 to 200,000 population (at typical average density) as being the maximum size for unrestrained car use, when car ownership approaches saturation. Many variables and assumptions affecting this conclusion have changed over the years; but experience from high car ownership countries in Europe confirms that in larger cities traffic restraint is unavoidable, no matter how much is invested in infrastructure, if the compactness, mixed use, and relatively high density are to be conserved. Evidence from the USA and Australia suggests that this limit of city size can rise, if densities are allowed to fall.

Eventually, however, a limit will be reached due to increasing trip lengths and other components of induced traffic in a decentralised urban area. In the larger British cities, which lack purpose-designed networks and where planning policies *are* geared to maintaining mixed uses and high densities, the inevitability of traffic restraint will have to be faced sooner rather than later. The *desirability* of such traffic restraint, to ensure a reasonable environment, comes sooner still. That point is passed already for Central and Inner London but is being reached in most of the larger provincial cities about now.

This crux (it must be said), which underscores the current dilemma over efforts to revitalise city central areas, has been "masked" by the effects of the recession, which has almost levelled out the growth curve of traffic over the last five years. The challenge for transport professionals, politicians and the public alike is to predict what is likely to happen as we emerge from recession and the "eye of the storm" is passed. In my view, for reasons of its statistically very strong relationship with real household income and the pent-up desire for more personal mobility, another surge in car ownership is likely; making more urgent the need for tough and effective policies of traffic restraint in the major urban centres.

Buchanan offered little or no prescriptive advice on this, for three reasons:

a. the presumption in his Report that society would opt for the maximum possible car use, by investing in new road networks and comprehensive 'traffic architectural' development;

b. the corollary to this, namely the eventual need for only a 'residual' or welfare role for public transport; and

c. a mistrust of the potential for road use pricing as a means of restraint.

On the first of these, society's rejection of comprehensive redevelopment has been emphatic, but car use continues to be embraced; on the second, the residual role for public transport is coming about, but for the wrong reasons (and its contribution to traffic restraint outside Central London is minimal); and on the third, it fell to Professor Smeed to report, one year after Buchanan in 1964, on the potential for road use pricing. The wilderness claimed his Report for more than 20 years but, with rapid technological advances in recent years, road use pricing seems to be firmly back on the agenda.

The possibilities are much canvassed now of new investment and priority being given to public transport, as a so-called 'positive' alternative to car use. But, with so little evidence that public transport can win even a rigged competition with the private car, this policy is a massive gamble. If, instead, it were linked to urban congestion pricing as the 'negative' restraint (if you will), where the revenues from the latter could be used to finance the former, one could begin to see some hope of a sustainable balance of transport demand in urban areas.

Two major difficulties stand in the way:

**a.** without planning intervention, the bus market will continue to decline in the face of rising car ownership and further decentralisation of land use activities; and

**b.** without public acceptance, the necessary legislation and political will to adopt traffic restraint measures will not be achieved.

So, before saying something about the help that Transport Telematics might yet bring to this, let us look back at the way circumstances have changed and transport policy has unfolded to get us to where we are now – on three crucial points:

**i.** the diminished powers and resources of local authorities, due to continuous reform and restructuring;

**ii.** the effects that bus deregulation and privatisation have had on patronage; and

**iii.** the implications of the public rejecting both further road building *and* traffic restraint.

## Local Authorities' Diminished Powers

Increasingly, over the years as traffic levels have risen, local government *has* (by and large) been given the necessary powers and responsibilities (although not always the resources) for controlling and managing urban street networks. During the 1960s and 1970s, an understanding did emerge that traffic management was necessarily part of the wider task of urban planning. Accordingly, local policies on development control, parking restrictions and traffic management (including priority measures for buses) were coordinated to achieve a balanced set of objectives. During the latter half of this period, a strategic dimension was given to this process through the metropolitan counties, whose remits were wider and technical resources greater than the districts or the smaller boroughs that preceded them. Amongst other things, they were able to collect data, so as to model travel demand at the conurbation scale, programme major highway improvements and channel increasing amounts of revenue support through the Passenger Transport Executives to public transport. In the case of the GLC, you will recall, they even dared to regulate the fares of London Transport and to finance the construction of the first section of the Jubilee Line, without the sanction of Government. Ironically, they had even proposed its continuation eastwards through Docklands ahead of development there (instead of nearly 10 years after the event!).

I would not want to paint too rosy a picture of that time, but there was a consensus (in the late 1970s) that transport and planning were (if not indissoluble) at least interrelated; there was a feeling that the complexity of interactions between land use activities, traffic and the local environment had been grasped; that the necessary powers were with the agencies appropriate to deal with them; and that strategic and longer term policies were essential to maintaining the desired balance between public and private transport. In short, by means of devolved powers *and* resources through the Transport Programmes and Policies/Transport Supplementary Grant mechanism (as it was originally conceived), the possibility of managing effectively the traffic problems in our larger urban areas was within reach. So, what went wrong? Well, the achilles' heel lay in the assumption that the balance could be maintained, on the one hand, by making a general open ended subsidy available to public transport and, on the other, by controlling the amount and price of *on*-street parking and of that minority of *off*-street car parks in public control. Both, in their different ways, very blunt instruments. Whatever one's view may be of the two tier metropolitan counties, at least they would have been better equipped, politically and technically, to face the now crucial question of traffic restraint, once the magnitude of future traffic growth was appreciated.

## The Dismantling of Planning Control

In one respect, the incoming government in 1979 was correct in its view that the open-ended subsidy of public transport could not go on indefinitely (revenue support across the country had reached £1,000m annually by 1985). However, the wisdom of what then followed has to be judged in the light of the situation in which we find ourselves now. The catalogue of change in the last fifteen years has been remorseless. All the bus services (outside London) have been deregulated and (almost everywhere) privatised; revenue support through the Transport Supplementary Grant has been withdrawn; and new bus grants terminated; the GLC and metropolitan counties were abolished; the Traffic Commissioners' role has been emasculated and the Passenger Transport Authorities given reduced powers. And, throughout the period, local authority finances generally have been squeezed and compulsory competitive tendering introduced. On top of that, we now have an emerging radical reform of the shire counties, too. Whatever the political inspiration was for each of these policies, together they have amounted to the unravelling of a previously coherent structure for planning and managing urban transport. The sophistication of what was set up during the 1970s may have been difficult to administer but at least it matched the complexity and interactions of the transport problem.

My concern is not so much with the success or failure of any one of these policy initiatives but the combined effect of all of them. This has been to diminish local authorities' control, to fragment responsibilities, to narrow and simplify the criteria for investment and to treat each of the elements of urban transport as if it were independent of the rest. In what I understand to be essentially an ideological argument over means, such aims as the reduction of public expenditure, the fostering of competition, the sharpening of price incentives, the avoidance of cross subsidy, and so on, all seem sensible in themselves. That is, until one realises that hardly any of it applies to the most important element of all, namely private car traffic. For all the arguments over regulation, ownership and the extent of government intervention in public transport have been conducted against a rapid escalation in private vehicle ownership, for which an almost entirely different set of rules apply.

The surge in car ownership, over the period 1984-90, should not have taken anyone by surprise. The immediate consequence of an economic boom during the latter half of the 1980s was a level of car-sales in UK exceeding two million per year. With real incomes rising at 3-4% per annum, car-ownership as a result grew (quite predictably) at 5-6% per annum. So much so, it took 5 years of recession 1990-94 (the longest in living memory) with a fall in real incomes, just to level out traffic growth. Until last year, new car sales were reduced to their 'steady replacement' level of about 1.6M per year. It is for this reason that I say we are in the 'eye of the storm' – for car-ownership is set to surge once again, just as soon as sustained growth of the economy resumes. (New car sales will probably top two million again in 1995). Indeed, one of the richer ironies is that output from the motor industry is usually regarded as an indicator of the strength of the economy as a whole. What is good for Nissan or Ford is somehow good for us all!

The new realism must surely be that, unless we adopt effective policies of 'positive' traffic restraint, the high growth forecasts for traffic can, and probably will, come about, determined almost wholly by rising real income per head. Congestion could influence to some extent where and when the major growth will occur, but *not* (with current policies) its magnitude overall. If the economy expands strongly during the late 1990s, then ownership could well exceed the high growth NRTF forecasts. (Even so, by the turn of the century UK car ownership would only have reached that prevailing in West Germany at the time of reunification). The potential for further traffic growth in this country is very considerable; that is why we have to *plan* rather than just leaving it either to chance or to the market.

## The Effects of Bus Deregulation on Patronage

It is also the background against which we must judge the contribution that bus deregulation has made. For all the upheaval which accompanied deregulation and privatisation, some of the longer run benefits of the 1985 Transport Act are clear – unit costs have fallen (although some of this is due to lower wages), restrictive labour practices have been curtailed, management and enterprise skills have been stimulated, the range of services offered (especially that of new minibuses) has been widened. Although competition has developed, it remains patchy. As to the other prime objective, total revenue support from public funds has fallen substantially. The casualties of deregulation have included the uncoordination of services, the woeful lack of passenger information, the stifling of technical innovation and the emerging trend towards private monopoly. Nevertheless, despite this, far from services being withdrawn, there are even some modest increases in bus-kms being run. Not a bad outcome, one might think, nine years after the event. But the real indicator that counts is patronage. For all the upheaval, the new services and extra mileage, passenger-kms are declining steadily 3-4% year on year. The outstanding exception, of course, is London, where London Buses has recorded increases in patronage. The irony in the fact that London is the only place (so far) to escape deregulation has not gone unnoticed!

The truth is, whatever achievements there may have been from implementing the 1985 Transport Act outside London (and I have outlined some of them), the effect on the secular long run (even terminal) decline of public transport has been minimal. In the big issue of how to control and manage competing demands for transport, bus deregulation has *at best* been a distraction. This is because the competition that matters is *not* between different bus operators but between private car traffic and public transport as a whole. That is the struggle being played out on the streets of our towns and cities every day, under a haphazard set of ground rules and conflicting objectives. Even where limiting the amount of private traffic in (say) a central area is one of the declared objectives, there is no clear policy mechanism by which that can be achieved. As things stand now, the only effective restraint is that of congestion, which is appallingly wasteful and hampers buses, cars and delivery vehicles alike, forcing up costs (estimated by the CBI to exceed £15bn p.a.) and degrading the environment. A market mechanism alone lacks both the breadth of vision and foresight required to stave off the decline of an essential public service.

In the absence of any consensus on positive traffic restraint (in particular, on direct forms of pricing) for congested areas, and in the light of the prospective increases in car ownership, the outlook for public transport (in particular buses) during the next 10 years is grim. The extra bus-kms cannot continue to be offered with average load factors falling; the profitability of marginal and off peak routes could continue to fall; and, as and when unemployment eases sufficiently, pressure on wage rates will begin to rise. When the time comes for small companies to renew their bus fleets, private capital to do so may be hard to find. But, most serious of all, within ten years of the 1985 Act being implemented, the overall public subsidy (through tendered services) could be back at the billion pound mark, but with 30-40% fewer passenger-kms. The alternative to subsidy at this level will be the progressive withdrawal of public transport from many existing towns and suburban areas, with bankruptcies and takeovers commonplace. Already, three or four dominant bus groups are emerging, so even the competition advantages may be lost.

## The Need for a Planning Framework

I am not arguing for a return to the days of indiscriminate subsidies and full blown regulation of public transport – experience, hard won over the last nine years, *has* shown us quite clearly how efficiency in public transport can be increased through clearer objectives and more direct incentives. But it *must* be within a coordinated framework and in conjunction with positive traffic restraint. There must be an authority (at regional or conurbation level) responsible for planning and forecasting the demand for services that are required and, through a suitable mixture of franchising and contract tendering, for ensuring an efficient supply. The same authority should be responsible for implementing parking control, priorities for buses and urban traffic management generally. Who knows, they might also be able to regulate Private Non-Residential parking and zone access controls.

Ideally, the costs of this should be met by the net revenues from a congestion pricing system applied to all traffic using the roads. I know this is looking ahead; but some of you will be aware of the research which is going on at Newcastle University, under my direction, into new techniques for 'automatic tolling' of vehicles, using short range microwave communications between moving vehicles and the road side. This is part of the European DRIVE programme for research into Transport Telematics. It will also enable much better techniques of traffic control and open up choices for vehicle users based upon reliable and up-to-date driver information.

Many people have argued that the new environmental concerns should be the mainspring of the case for traffic restraint. Although in my view it is an added reason, relief of congestion is a far more compelling one. But I can appreciate how stressing the environmental case may be an easier way of "selling" a restraint policy – since people seem to understand more readily how *their* vehicle contributes to pollution than to congestion. Nevertheless, the real costs to industry and commerce arise through increasing delays and the unreliability of deliveries. For this reason, future charging for the use of road space needs to be directly related to the congestion that is caused. Merely adding more tax to fuel prices would be a poor proxy for congestion pricing based upon marginal social cost. (Incredibly, the Royal Commission failed to consider congestion costs, on the grounds that they did not meet their definition of 'external costs' of road use!). In any case, since environmental costs and congestion costs are both generated by traffic in urban areas, both should be charged for separately, by appropriate means that relate as closely as possible to the actual amounts of each cost incurred.

## Public Rejection of Major Road Building

Before concluding, I must say something about the building of new roads. Partly through appalling decisions like Twyford Down and partly through the questionable tactics of direct action protest groups, the issue now looms large in the debate. The statement that "most people... agree that building our way out of congestion is unacceptable and impractical" seems to imply a halt to all *new* road building. I am uneasy with this. In particular, with the assumption that, where it is physically possible and justifiable in economic terms to expand road infrastructure, this should *not* be done for global environmental reasons. The opening in 1991, for example, of the Newcastle Western Bypass, including the new Blaydon Bridge across the Tyne and the Woolsington Bypass leading to Newcastle Airport – a £100m capital investment in the region's road network – had provided a welcome boost to industry and, at the same time, help to relieve hard pressed environmental areas. And, although the benefits of these new roads are being felt in the suburban and industrial areas of the city, it does not in any way contradict the need either for further traffic restraint in the central areas of Newcastle and Gateshead or for improving public transport in the conurbation. Well designed roads have an important *complementary* role to play, alongside other policies in the transportation package. There is an extraordinary myth evolving that, if we stop building new roads, we will *in consequence* stop any further growth in traffic. As a co-author of SACTRA's 1994 report on 'induced traffic', I must warn of the folly of this idea.

As to the impacts of new road construction on the environment, they are many and various, and the (net) balance of them can be either positive or negative, depending on the nature of the impacts, how they are assessed and valued, and who trades them off to determine the balance (SACTRA's 1992 report dwelt on this). For example, in the current national roads programme, there are about 200 bypass schemes for towns and villages on existing roads. On almost any criteria, except (of course) where the new alignment might encroach on a National Park (say) or a Site of Special Scientific Interest, a net gain both environmentally and economically is likely to accrue. Moreover, the communities affected have often been waiting years for such bypasses (Newbury is a classic case in point).

The same can often be true of town centre relief roads, especially where wholesale pedestrianisation can be achieved as a result. This is a particular case of a more general principle where highway investment is focused on infrastructural renewal/replacement, rather than merely expansion. The crux is providing not *more* roads but *better* ones, the new roads being purpose designed to carry predefined traffic flows, segregated from other activities and freed from congestion, while the old roads are assigned to other purposes (such as access, parking, public transport priority, or even recreation). The key to both area wide safety and environmental schemes using traffic calming techniques may often be found in local highway improvements. The objective need not be to expand the traffic capacity of a network but merely to raise the efficiency and safety with which it operates.

## Telematics to the Rescue?

The same is true of applying advanced Transport Telematics techniques of inter-active traffic control, dynamic route guidance and so on. They have got to be planned in conjunction with traffic calming and restraint measures; making the main distributary network more efficient and (at the same time) raising the price of car use and protecting the environment of residential areas and town centres. As we survey the impressive range of potential applications of Telematics to transport problems, it is clear that almost all of them will bear on the efficiency and safety of operating traffic systems (to the benefit of the users). However, the most promising developments – such as dynamic route guidance, parking information/booking, interactive urban traffic control, Radio Data System/Traffic Message Channel traffic information and variable message signs – whilst raising network efficiency and minimising congestion costs, will (on balance) encourage car use rather than restrain it.

So far as I can see, only *three* telematics applications will serve a policy of traffic restraint. These are: public transport information systems, on-line pre-trip planning systems and road use pricing/automatic debiting systems. Accordingly, these are the more important developments, in terms of strategic transport policy, as car use continues to expand.

Eventually, however, patterns of trip-making will be more strongly influenced by the development of telecommunications. The full blown effects of teleworking, teleconferencing and tele-shopping on the daily lives of ordinary citizens remain to be seen but, within a few years, these more profound challenges for transport and planning professionals will have to be faced. The hope is that much of the present demand for person movement can be substituted by more sophisticated communication devices, with congestion becoming "a thing of the past". In the meantime, the prospect of another doubling of traffic levels by 2025 A.D. is very real and has to be faced.

# System Problems and Incremental Solutions

## Can the Foresight exercise help?

**Dr Christopher Elliott**

Director, Smith System Engineering Ltd

Royal Academy of Engineering Charter Professor
of Engineering Design, University of Bristol

## Personal Profile

After a first degree in Natural Sciences and a PhD in experimental physics, Dr Elliott joined Smith System Engineering in 1976. Since then he has worked in electronic warfare, automation and the application of parallel computing to everything from radar to fingerprint recognition. His work for the last ten years has been mainly on the design, management and economics of complex systems, using space exploration as a model.

Chris Eliott is also a Royal Academy of Engineering Charter Professor of Engineering Design at the University of Bristol and is Honorary Secretary of the Foundation for Science and Technology.

# System Problems and Incremental Solutions

## Can the Foresight exercise help?

### Dr Christopher Elliott

## Introduction

Sustainable Development can only be achieved if the decisions about changes in society are informed and logical. This is especially true for transport, where the decisions have a dual effect on sustainable development:

- a direct effect, whereby the wrong choice leads directly to environmental damage

- an indirect effect, whereby the wrong choice impoverishes society through poor mobility.

Design engineers have a crucial contribution to make, by ensuring:

- that decisions are rooted in analysis, not emotion

- that transport is treated as a system, not components

- that Foresight considers solutions, not technologies.

## Rational decisions

Let us examine the rational basis for two recent urban transport decisions taken in the UK – the electric buses used in Oxford and the Manchester Metrolink.

Electric buses are promoted, like other electric vehicles, because they are non-polluting. Oxford's buses have a range of 55 miles on fully charged batteries. If we assume that the efficiency of the electricity grid is 95% the battery charger is 90% efficient and the thermal efficiency of the power station is 40%, electric buses consume 12.2 MJoule per mile. A diesel minibus will do 10 miles per gallon in hilly cities and 15 mpg in a flat city like Oxford. This corresponds to 11.3 MJoule per mile.

This trivial calculation is not accurate enough to say that electric buses use more energy. What it does show is that care is needed before stating that they are less polluting because they use less energy and that electric vehicles are unlikely to make a significant contribution to a non-polluting transport strategy. Oxford Bus Company says that "... electric buses will play a key role in improving Oxford's city centre environment" but is that only by moving the pollution out of the city to a distant power station?

Manchester Metrolink is an example of a modern tracked urban transit system. There are two arguments advanced for such systems – energy efficiency and social utility. Consider first the energy efficiency, when compared with a double deck bus. Energy is consumed by three mechanisms:

- aerodynamic drag

- rolling resistance of the wheels

- kinetic energy (lost in braking).

Each of these may be calculated from knowledge of the properties of each vehicle (Reference 1 and Annex). Let us use as an indicator the energy used to transport one passenger between two stops, one kilometre apart, at a maximum speed of 50 km per hour (30 mph).

If each vehicle is full, the energy used by Metrolink is:

- aerodynamic drag – 434 kJoule

- rolling resistance – 416 kJoule

- acceleration – 6270 kJoule

making a total of 35.6 kJoule per passenger. The bus uses 557, 1320 and 2123 kJoule respectively, making 40 kJoule per passenger. It would appear that, at rush hour when all vehicles are full, slightly less energy is used by the train (but do not forget the inefficiencies of electrical generation and transmission for the trains).

The position is very different if the vehicles are not full. With 20 passengers, the Metrolink train requires 263 kJoule and a bus requires 137 kJoule per passenger for a 1 km journey. Off-peak services make trains look a lot less attractive. The need for a transport service to cover not just the rush hours but also the slack periods will be discussed in the next section of this paper.

If the energy argument for trains is suspect, what about social utility? A bus which runs on dedicated lanes within the city centre is free to exploit the flexibility of steering to provide a more responsive service in the suburbs. A train can only follow the tracks laid down for it. It can be argued that this inflexibility makes the train more predictable (you know that it will always stop only at stations, whereas buses can go anywhere) but the idea of deliberately reducing the flexibility and responsiveness of a service cannot make sense in the long term.

Trains appear to benefit still from an historical accident. George Stephenson realised that Newcomen's steam engine could form the basis of a vehicle in 1813, before McAdam was appointed to build modern roads (1827), Dunlop perfected the pneumatic tyre (1888) and Ackermann's steering linkage was demonstrated (1878). Stephenson had no choice but to run his engine on rails at the beginning of the 19th century but that is no reason to do the same as we enter the 21st century. The European Commission has a task force studying *The train of the future* – this argument would suggest that it will have rubber tyres and be steerable.

## Complex or complicated?

Decision makers are used to dealing with problems that are **complicated**, meaning rich in **detail.** Whether they are trying to manage a computer or a farm, a football crowd or a multi-national company, managers know how to get the task done – break the problem down into its constituent parts, get an expert to solve each part, and stitch the whole together with a management hierarchy.

This approach falls down when it is applied to problems that are **complex**, meaning rich in **structure**. For these problems, a decision about one part of the problem affects the behaviour of another part of the problem and the problem must be considered as a whole. Such problems are referred to as systems. One of the formal definitions of a system is that it is a set of components which, when brought together, exhibit properties which are not present in the components alone ("emergent properties").

One of the most elegant examples of a system is the human body. None of the components (heart, lungs, brain, muscles...) exhibit the special property of the whole – life – and all are needed before that property emerges.

We refer routinely to "transport systems" without apparently realising the importance of this concept of wholeness for their management. Two trivial examples will illustrate this in action.

There is a famous example (Figure 1) known as the Braess paradox (Reference 2). This considers a simple road network, some roads of which are congested (defined to mean that each extra car increases journey time of other cars). Assume that each driver selects the route from A to D that minimises his journey time.

It takes a fixed time to drive from A to B or from C to D of 50 minutes (ie those roads are not congested). The time to drive from A to C or B to D will be assumed to be 5n minutes, where n is the number of cars using the road per minute. If each driver chooses the best route for him, an equal number go down each branch. With 10 cars per minute (5 per branch), each journey lasts 75 minutes.

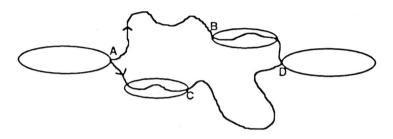

**10 cars per minute cars travel from A to D**
**A-B and C-D are uncongested - journey takes 50 minutes**
**B-D and A-C are congested - journey takes 5 x n minutes (n cars per minute)**

**each driver exercises free choice:**
**equilibrium is with 5 cars taking each route - 75 minutes each**

**Figure 1** Road network

What happens if we add an extra road, a by-pass from B to C which is uncongested and takes 10 minutes? The first driver to reach C, knowing that C to D will take 50 minutes, takes the by-pass and then B to D. The total time for that car is now (25 + 10 + 30) = 65 minutes instead of 75 – a significant improvement. The other 5 cars per minute using B to D now take 80 minutes. In equilibrium, where everyone chooses the route which minimises their journey time, 8 cars per minute use A to C, 6 of them take the by-pass and each journey takes 90 minutes. In other words, the by-pass has increased the journey time for everyone and increased the traffic on the congested roads!

Is this realistic? The model relating time to number of cars per minute on roads B-D and A-C is simple but might represent a "back double" through a housing estate – short but very congested. Similar results are obtained with more complicated networks and more realistic time models. They are also found in practice. Shortly after Braess first described this paradox, it was observed and studied in Stuttgart. Closer to home, a recent article in *The Times* on the proposed Newbury by-pass stated that "the extraordinary conclusion is that overall congestion could get worse" (Reference 3).

The more general point is that by allowing each driver the freedom to pick the route that is optimum for him, the time taken by everybody (including him) rises. The "market" has found a stable optimum that is worse for everybody.

Let us now look at a different kind of network, a train service linking several stations. We will make the network simple, consisting of six stations along a single line:

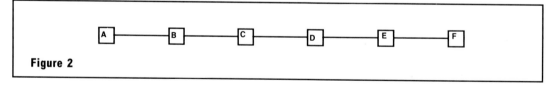

**Figure 2**

The line from C to D is particularly expensive to build and operate. It requires a revenue of £10 000 per day to break even whereas all of the other lines require only £3 000.

Assume that 1 000 passengers per day wish to travel between any pair of stations and will pay a return fare of £1 per stop (for example, 1 000 per day wish to go between A and D and will pay £3 return, a further 1 000 wish to go between A and E and will pay £4 and so on). The total revenue earned by the network is £35 000 per day and its total running cost is £22 000 per day – a viable proposition.

Now let us look at each line in turn. A-B and E-F both earn £5 000 and cost £3 000 per day. B-C and D-E both earn £8 000 and cost £3 000. These lines are all profitable. C to D however makes a loss of £1 000 per day since it only earns £9 000.

The obvious action is to close down this loss-making line and keep the profitable ones but then the other lines lose the passengers who were on journeys which crossed from C to D. The number of passengers using each of the other lines falls to 2 000 per day, with the result that they all lose money and must be closed down.

This simple network illustrates clearly the more general principle that one cannot consider elements of a transport system in isolation. A perfectly viable network can include non-viable elements and, if they are eliminated, the network may itself become non-viable. The solution is simple – the section from C to D has to levy a charge on the other sections but can that be reconciled with a policy of no cross subsidies? 'Cherry picking' the profitable routes results in a collapse of the network.

A similar argument can be applied to the distribution of services in time rather than space. The late night commuter trains which are largely empty are necessary to persuade passengers to use the daytime trains. It was shown above that an urban train system may be energy efficient when fully loaded but not for lightly loaded off peak services.

## Foresight as a planning tool

Where does Technology Foresight fit in, given that the decisions on both the elements of a transport system and the system itself are not always rational? The report of the recent Technology Foresight Programme of Transport (Reference 4) recognised these issues. Its Executive Summary states:

> "For the UK and its major competitors, the route to the practical application of technologies in transport is rarely straightforward. **The policy context is key.** Most applications require the integration of technologies from a variety of industries to serve markets which typically cut across the public and private sectors."

The report makes several recommendations that address directly the issues raised in this paper. It recognises implicitly that the inflexibility of tracked transport has one great benefit identified above – predictability. Its *Informed Traveller* project aims to use information technology to allow passengers and transport operators to take full benefit of a flexible combination of public and private services using tracked or steered vehicles whilst achieving the predictability of trains.

Its specific research recommendations are directed towards solving system problems, either in the form of a complete vehicle (*The Foresight Vehicle*) or regarding urban centres as a system (*Clear Zones*). The greatest number of specific recommendations are the System Research Priorities, including social and economic issues such as the need to travel and improved dynamic modelling of transport systems.

These projects do have a role in ensuring that transport has the minimum environmental impact but the report recognises that technology can only contribute within the context of a transport policy.

## Conclusions

This paper has demonstrated three points:

- that decisions on transport systems must be informed by rational analysis and not just emotional or historical considerations;
- that transport policy must consider transport as a system and that local decisions based on local market forces can lead to everyone losing;

- that the Transport Foresight exercise addressed these constraints and has recommended ways of tackling them, recognising that its terms of reference were technology foresight and not broader policy issues.

Sustainable development of a transport infrastructure that meets the future needs of society needs a broader vision than is offered by emotional or market forces. Engineering and engineers have a critical role to ensure that rational decisions are taken - decisions that reflect the physical reality of complex problems and not merely historical accident or political fashion.

## References

1  Elliott C J *Turning dreams into specifications*, Engineering Management Journal, Feb1993

2  Cohen J E *The counterintuitive in conflict and cooperation*, American Scientist, 76, Nov 1988, pp 577-584

3  *Accelerating on the road to a fiasco*, The Times, 26 July 1995

4  *Progress through partnership – 5: Transport*, HMSO, 1995, ISBN 0-11-430116-6

## Acknowledgements

Information used in this paper was kindly provided by:

- British Rail Research
- Metrolink
- MIRA - the Motor Industry Research Association
- The Oxford Bus Company

## Annex

The further assumptions used in the calculations of the energy performance of various vehicles were as follows:

*Oxford Bus* — battery capacity: 280AHr @ 228V

*Diesel Minibus* — calorific value of fuel: 1.69MJ per gallon

*Metrolink train*
— mass empty: 45 tonne
— max number of passengers: 200
— rolling resistance: 6.4 N tonne-1
— frontal area: 9 m²
— drag coefficient: 0.5

*Double deck bus*
— mass empty: 12 tonne
— max number of passengers: 100
— rolling resistance: 60 N tonne-1
— frontal area: 10 m²
— drag coefficient: 0.55

*Mass of each passenger (inc luggage)*
— 100 kg

# The Realities of Managing Car Dependence

**David Worskett FIHT**

Director of Public Affairs
RAC Motoring Services

## Personal Profile

**David Worskett** joined the RAC as Director of Public Affairs in September 1989, after 15 years as a civil servant, mostly with the UK Department of Transport.

Between 1987 and 1989 he was Head of Road Safety at the UK Department, playing a major role in establishing the UK Government's target of reducing casualties by a third by the year 2000, and in the production of the 1989 White Paper on *The Road User and the Law*.

His government experience included extensive negotiations in the European Community on a wide range of transport issues, including a key role in the drive to liberalise air transport.

A Fellow of the Institution of Highways and Transportation, and of the Institution of the Motor Industry, he has steered the RAC towards a 'centre ground' position on environmental issues relating to road transport, and sees those issues as central to the development of transport policy in the years ahead. He has also focused attention on getting better value for money out of the existing road system, and on the concept that roads are a public sector service just like any other, and should be seen in the same light.

# The Realities of Managing Car Dependence

## David Worskett FIHT

In the time available, this clearly cannot be a detailed or very profound review of the role of cars in developed western societies, or future trends in car use. However, I hope that I can provide a few useful thoughts to stimulate discussion. This session is about the role of the engineer in finding a sustainable transport policy, and a consumer perspective is indispensable, particularly on environmental issues which so directly affect consumers', voters', lives. I have been asked to try to define what the consumer – the road user – actually *wants* of engineers. That is not easy, given that the truthful answer is 'to have conflicting objectives fully reconciled'.

Let me start by putting on the table four basic realities about transport policy, without which debate will be largely fruitless.

The first reality is that we have a significant environmental problem, as a result of the amount of transport our society needs. But the nature of the environmental problem is frequently wrongly analysed and wrongly stated, with the result that the proposed solutions too often address minor rather than major problems, or do so in the wrong way.

The second reality is that transport is demand led. It does not, for the most part, happen for its own sake. Transport is needed to serve markets, to deliver goods, to allow people to go about their work, or to give them access to personal or leisure activities and tasks. So when we talk about 'demand management', as we increasingly do, we need to debate not what sort of transport or how much of it we want, but which aspects of demand we propose to manage.

There is, of course, a glittering prize for transport policy – a holy grail – where economic growth is actually separated from transport growth, but we are nowhere near finding it. If we could find it, there would be relatively little difficulty about 'sustainability'. For the moment however, there is a problem. Graph A relates traffic growth to GDP.

The third reality is that road transport has come to dominate both the commercial and the personal transport sectors because it is the most cost effective, the most flexible, the least vulnerable to institutionalised disruption, and the mode which most amply meets personal aspirations and broadens human choice. Graph B shows modal split today.

The fourth reality is that there are several different transport markets. Different policies and solutions are needed for each, but we need to be clear that, except for the urban situation, road transport will continue to grow, and will continue to dominate. The task therefore is to make quite sure that it does so in the most environmentally acceptable way possible.

Let us look at the first reality.

I said that the environmental problems were real, but often wrongly identified. Let me tell you what I believe the major and so far unresolved environmental problems relating to road transport are, and indeed what they are not.

They are *not*, for the *future*, really about the so-called regulated pollutants – nitrous oxides, sulphur dioxides and the like. Automotive technology has already hugely reduced the output per vehicle of these pollutants: a modern car produces 90% fewer of them than its predecessor of 20 or 30 years ago did. Graph C shows how levels of nitrogen oxide from motor vehicles are already declining, as our vehicle fleets are modernised. Modernisation is largely to do with better engine management systems and catalytic converters. Of course there will always be problem vehicles – what we in the UK now call 'gross polluters' but they will be a small minority –probably not more than 10% of the vehicle population – and indeed must be dealt with by tough enforcement measures. A case of stick rather than carrot, I fear.

# The Challenge for Transport

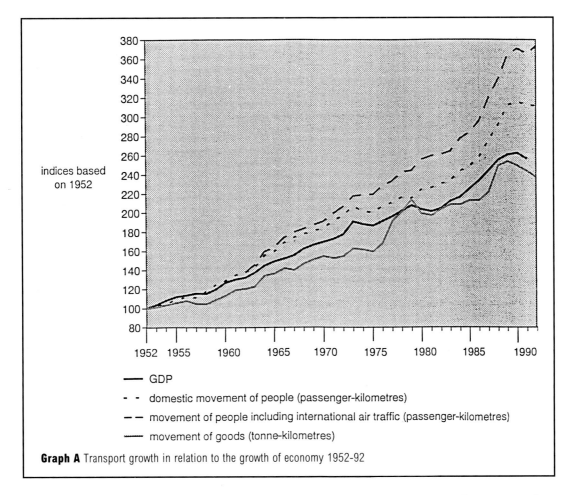

indices based on 1952

— GDP

- - domestic movement of people (passenger-kilometres)

— — movement of people including international air traffic (passenger-kilometres)

•••••• movement of goods (tonne-kilometres)

**Graph A** Transport growth in relation to the growth of economy 1952-92

This sort of technological progress will undoubtedly continue, and we shall see further improvements. So while in some parts of Western Europe and the United States urban air quality is currently a major environmental priority, it need not be so and will not be so for long. Nor indeed, taking a medium term view will the problems of black smoke and particulates, predominantly from diesel vehicles be a long term difficulty. New technology will come to the rescue there as well.

The degree of muddle on this subject is only too well illustrated by the Chief Executive of a very important British local authority, who had better remain nameless, who fairly recently wrote a piece for a major newspaper expressing the gravest concern about the problem caused by black smoke in his urban area. He was right about the problem, but unfortunately he then went on to propose banning all cars as the remedy, and black smoke is almost entirely the product of heavy diesels, coming in particular from goods vehicles and badly maintained older buses. Our thinking has to be clearer than that.

So what do I think the major environmental problems are for which solutions are still too uncertain for us to feel at all comfortable. There are three:

We are a long way from really being able to tackle the $CO_2$ problem, as Graph D shows. It is possible to over-react to the fears about global warming, but it would be quite wrong of us not to react at all. However, the best, and most recent work done in the United States universities suggests to any rational being that while steps must be taken to reduce $CO_2$ output, by reducing fossil fuel and energy consumption from all sectors, we can afford to take a little more time over finding the right solutions, thus minimising any possible adverse impact on our economies, and maximising our chances of maintaining the economic growth which will in turn allow us to pay for the environmental measures which are needed.

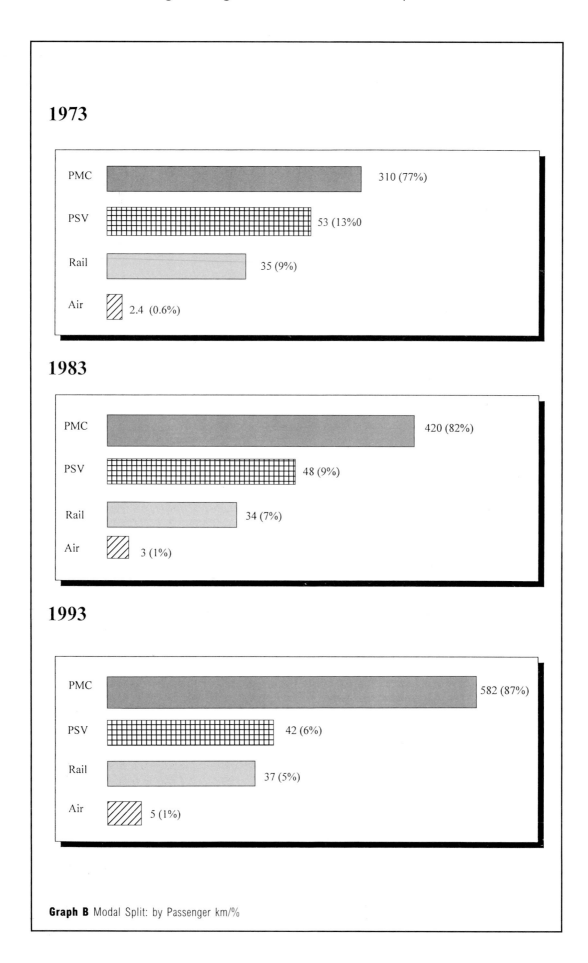

**1973**

| | |
|---|---|
| PMC | 310 (77%) |
| PSV | 53 (13%0 |
| Rail | 35 (9%) |
| Air | 2.4 (0.6%) |

**1983**

| | |
|---|---|
| PMC | 420 (82%) |
| PSV | 48 (9%) |
| Rail | 34 (7%) |
| Air | 3 (1%) |

**1993**

| | |
|---|---|
| PMC | 582 (87%) |
| PSV | 42 (6%) |
| Rail | 37 (5%) |
| Air | 5 (1%) |

**Graph B** Modal Split: by Passenger km/%

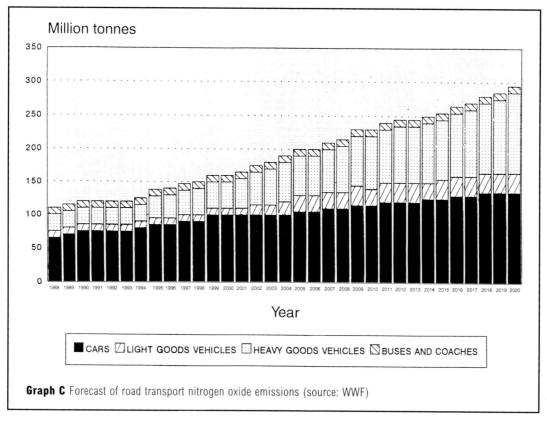

**Graph C** Forecast of road transport nitrogen oxide emissions (source: WWF)

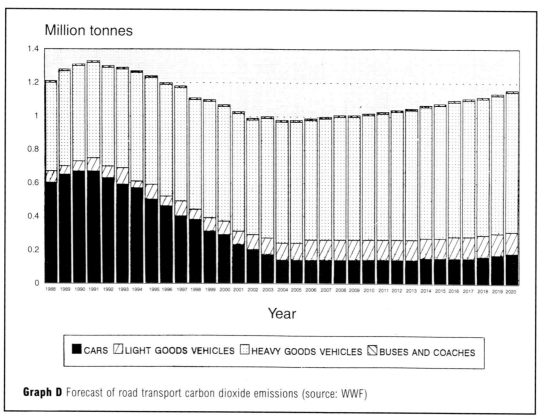

**Graph D** Forecast of road transport carbon dioxide emissions (source: WWF)

**The Foresight Vehicle:**

- **"Development of a vehicle which is significantly more environmentally friendly yet meets mass market expectations"**

- **"Reduce greenhouse gases by half, and eliminate toxic emissions"**

- **"Meet current consumer expectations for performance and payload"**

- **"Radical reduction in vehicle weight without compromising safety and security"**

- **"Utilise 'control by wire', 'active safety systems', lightweight materials"**

**Chart E** The Foresight Vehicle

The only way forward on the $CO_2$ front is by reducing fuel consumption of vehicles. But if we are to give consumers the sorts of vehicles which they want, with the sort of performance characteristics which they want, we are going to need a new approach to vehicle design and technology.

The recent British Technology Foresight Review (Chart E) carried out under the auspices of the British Cabinet Office, and modelled on similar exercises conducted successfully over many years in Japan, identified the development of new lightweight materials for vehicles (in all models incidentally) as a common vital requirement for transport in the next century. Commercially viable lightweight materials for vehicles will then open the way to down-sizing of engines, with step changes in fuel efficiency, but without steps backward in terms of performance characteristics. They will, however, also require new approaches to safety – collision avoidance systems and the like. In all the discussions about the environment we must never forget that 'safety' is the biggest 'quality of life' factor of all – and there is a worrying tendency to overlook that fact.

The next unresolved environmental problem is noise, and this is closely related to the sheer number of vehicles likely to be on the roads even if we assume that traffic growth can be held to minimum forecast levels, rather than the somewhat frightening maximum levels which some forecasts have predicted.

In some countries in Western Europe, traffic noise is already back on the agenda having disappeared for some years. I predict that where it is not, it soon will be. With more and more vehicles, the scale of the noise intrusion into people's every day lives will undoubtedly become less and less acceptable.

So priority number one for engineers – in this case engineers dealing with mechanical, electronic, and materials engineering – must be to deliver, at affordable prices, vehicles which conquer, through technical innovation, the unsolved problems I have identified.

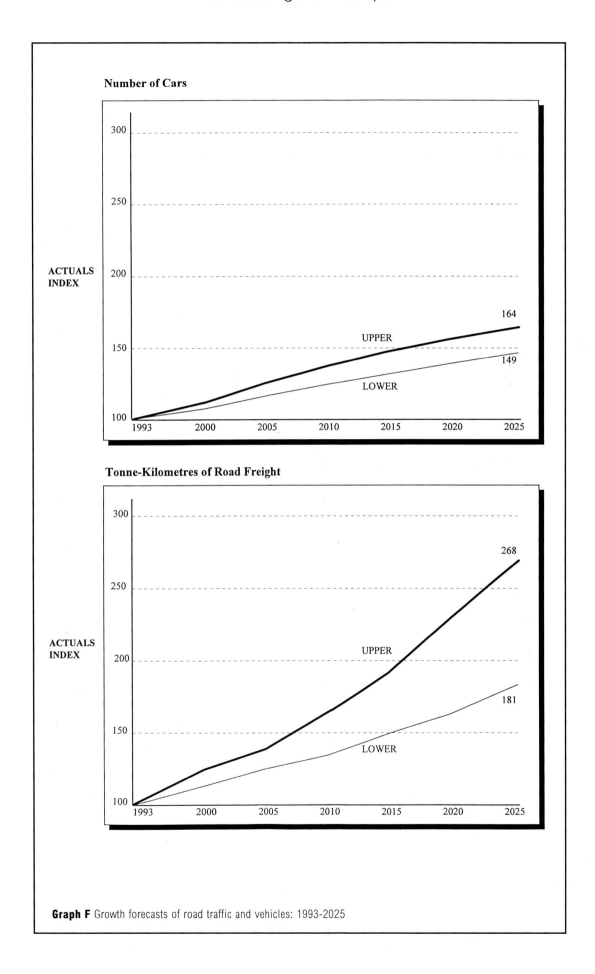

**Graph F** Growth forecasts of road traffic and vehicles: 1993-2025

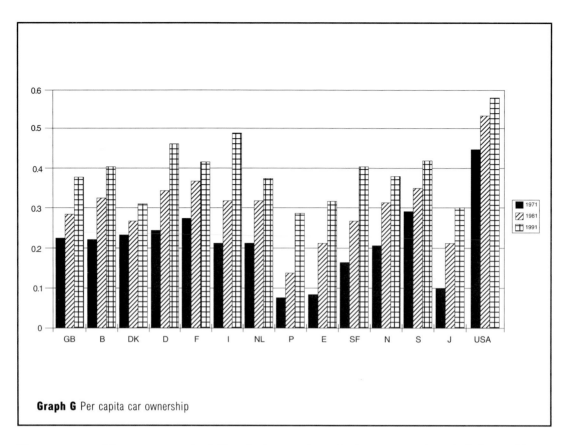

**Graph G** Per capita car ownership

However, to achieve true sustainability the innovative solutions cannot just shift the problems elsewhere, and they cannot, in overall economic terms, be more costly to society than are the problems they set out to overcome.

The second and third realities are that transport is demand led and that road transport has come to dominate. If we adopt a 'business as usual' scenario, demand is going to lead to a fundamental problem over the 'sheer number' of vehicles on our roads, with unacceptable consequences for congestion, and for disruption of communities. Graph F is the well known range of traffic forecasts.

In order to dispel any illusions that the UK is unique, or that we performed relatively badly in managing this process, allow me to spend two minutes on some international comparisons.

In reality there is not much difference between developed western societies in this respect.

Graph G shows per capita car ownership in 14 OECD countries for the years 1971, 1981 and 1991. In all of them car ownership has increased steadily, and differences between the countries have narrowed. While the United States has much higher levels of car ownership, its lead over European countries in this respect is much reduced. It is also clear that growth in car ownership has been particularly high in those countries which have had the most rapid growth in gross domestic product – Italy, Spain, Portugal and Japan.

There is relatively little difference between any of these countries in terms of their reliance on the car. Graph H shows that most developed countries rely on cars for between 75-80% of land passenger transport, and shows the changes in reliance between 1981 and 1991.

At one end of the scale the US car reliance for land passenger transport stands out at 98%; while at the other Japan makes least use of cars relative to other modes, at 53%. It is interesting that in the United States, and in the Netherlands, there has been virtually no growth in the car's share of growth of total distance travelled over the period. One might reasonably speculate that in the United States this is because at no point, during the period, have there

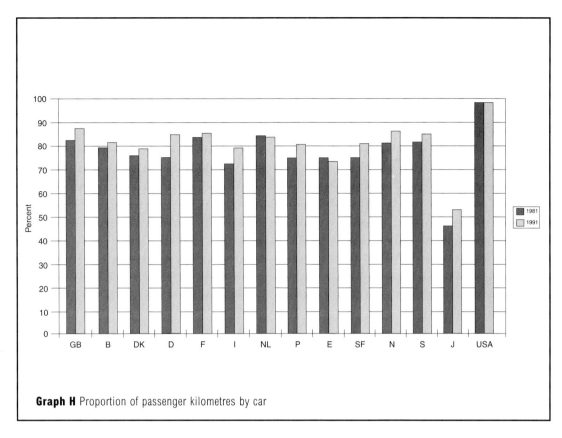

**Graph H** Proportion of passenger kilometres by car

been many realistic alternatives, while in the Netherlands it may be because there have always been a reasonable number of realistic alternatives.

However, I would suggest to you that even from these very cursory international comparisons one message is clear. That is that we must not deceive ourselves about the scope for non-road forms of transport to supplant road transport to any very great extent. Whatever policies are pursued there seems to be a large 'block' of travel for which people are dependent on their cars. Even where countries have relatively less dependence on road transport, that dependence, seen as a proportion of all transport in the country concerned, remains very high, and the clear linkage to increasing gross domestic product seems to imply that road traffic will continue to grow at a considerable rate.

The message for engineers, in respect of the 'second reality', is that because much of the dependence on road transport is both economically rational and probably irreversible, technical and physical measures will be needed on a growing scale to manage and accommodate it.

We need to understand better why and how we have become so dependent on road transport, and in particular on the car in order to manage the problem. I ought to say that my own organisation, the RAC, has a major research project on this running at the moment, at the Oxford Transport Studies Unit, and I hope that we shall be able to throw light on the problem later in the autumn, when the report from that study is ready. However, one can easily enough suggest some of the things we need to look at.

First, it is clear that land use planning has a major role to play. The more we distribute our activities, whether they are work places, super-markets, or leisure centres, around our towns and cities, and in the countryside, the more we generate a requirement for flexible personal transport so that people can achieve access to them.

Second, the changing nature of employment is significant. We live in an age when people change jobs more often than ever before, and are more likely to be made redundant than

**Factors in 'Structural Dependence':**

* **land use and locational policies and decisions**

* **changing employment patterns and requirements**

* **female participation in the workforce**

* **changing patterns of school and welfare provision**

* **emerging social groups and demographic change**

**Chart I** Factors in 'Structural Dependence'

ever before. Frequent changes in employment generate frequent changes in journey patterns. Changes in jobs simply cannot always be matched by changes in where people live. For a start, a partner may still be ideally located for access to his/her job. And maybe the children are well established in the right school. So maybe a longer, awkward car journey in order to get you to a new place of work is the only practicable option. Greater use of home working through telecommunications could be helpful in this respect in the medium term but the validity of this concept is so far wholly unproven.

Third, there are profound social changes taking place. Much higher proportions of women now work, but more often than not retain the lead role in running the household and caring for the children. In reality time constraints are such that the different roles can only be combined and successfully run together by using the flexibility and efficiency provided by a car. The car is likely to be particularly necessary for the new "emerging social groups" – working women, single parent families, and the growing proportion of active elderly, and active disabled people.

Factors such as these are perhaps best characterised by the term "structural dependence" (Chart I). What then is the role of the engineer in helping to tackle it? It seems to me that it is not for engineers to solve many of these problems or indeed the more subjective aspects such as fear of violence on our public transport systems, or when walking back from the tube to home late at night. These are all social issues rather than technical ones, and I do not think the scope of this conference extends to 'social engineering'.

There are, however, things engineers can do to help reduce 'dependence' on cars, at least at the margin. In our urban areas, civil engineers must continue to seek ways of fitting 'alternative' infrastructure into our old street networks. We need cycleways; we need better footways; maybe we need trams or Light Rapid Transit Systems. But if their introduction simply causes the traffic to snarl up even more, little will have been gained.

We need more attention to detail. So many traffic problems can be solved if a trained highways or traffic engineer can find time simply to study, in detail, exactly what is happening on an

**Transport Market Segmentation**

Some Examples:

| | |
|---|---|
| • **children** | |
| • **family with children** | |
| • **single parent family** | **urban** |
| • **urban low income** | |
| • **urban high income** | **suburban** |
| • **rural low income** | |
| • **rural high income** | **interurban** |
| • **elderly/retired** | |
| • **disabled** | **rural community** |
| • **with access to car** | |
| • **without access to car** | **rural** |

**Chart J** Transport market segmentation: some examples

urban road, and especially at the junctions. Junction management seems to me to hold some of the same prospects for low cost alleviation of congestion as Accident Investigation and Prevention schemes have done for safety.

But we may need, also, a return to the courage and vision in respect of major projects shown by civil engineers of earlier generations – and only seen in this country in the context of building the Channel Tunnel, and the Dartford and Severn second crossings.

One of the secrets of success in managing urban traffic is to provide the infrastructure to separate the through traffic from the local traffic.

That is what the Oslo pricing scheme has allowed to happen.

That is what the tunnels achieve in Dusseldorf.

That is what the Paris tunnels are meant for.

Where are the schemes for the UK's cities?

The third 'reality' was that people, for good reason, choose private transport because it is the most efficient means of achieving their current lifestyles, and because they prefer it.

What engineers can and must do, however, is to speak out when they are asked to solve problems which are *not* for them to solve. The unpleasantness of offensive graffiti at bus stops may be reduced by use of graffiti resistant paint, but the paint is a sticking plaster, not a cure for the underlying problem.

Lastly, we come to the fourth reality, which is essentially about market segmentation: urban, sub-urban, inter-urban, rural communities, and wholly rural. In each of the locational segments there are a wide variety of different types of transport use.

You will notice that this is a longer, more complex, list than usual. That is because I believe that the transport market has been grossly over simplified in much recent debate. Transport 'engineers' have a responsibility to ensure that this tendency to oversimplify does not lead

---

**The Role of the Engineer:**

- **new technologies, designs, materials**

- **adaptation of urban infrastructure**

- **attention to detail – junction management**

- **specific solutions for specific problems**

- **creativity and lateral thinking about
  "best practicable environmental options"**

- **frankness about what engineers can't do**

- **faith in grand concepts**

- **application of professional, scientific knowledge and integrity**

**Chart K** The role of the engineer

---

to major lack of realism about the extent to which any one 'solution' can be applied to different situations.

The importance of detailed market segmentation is related to the importance of understanding why certain groups are in certain locations so heavily "car dependent". We must ask ourselves whether we can realistically hope to change the direction of the social trends which have given rise to this dependence, or whether the right thing to do is to accommodate it.

The achievement of a sustainable transport policy will require the application of different solutions and policies to the very different, urban, inter-urban and rural situations. The criteria for choosing solutions should be hard-headed economic appraisal, together with application of the "best *practicable* environmental option". That needs to apply to vehicles as much as to transport infrastructure and operations.

It is in the development of the "best practicable environmental option" that I think the engineer has another key role to play.

For these purposes I take it as a 'given' that our society must go on constructing infrastructure. There are some who would disagree fundamentally with that view, on environmental grounds, but that is not the issue I want to address today.

It is important to remember that opposition to infrastructure has become increasingly vocal, and powerful, almost regardless of the mode of transport involved. The line of the Channel Tunnel rail link is every bit as contentious as the Newbury By-pass.

Engineers cannot remove the fundamentalist objections and protestations. Nor can they reverse a social trend which seems to involve more and more people seeking to impose their own views after, and on top of, due processes of law, established by the proper democratic process.

What engineers can do is to assist in reducing the scale and validity of such action by helping to identify and design the "best practicable environmental options".

For roads, this may mean a radical look at design standards for by-passes, so that the desire on the part of the local residents for a by-pass is not delayed or thwarted by objections to the design of the by-pass itself.

For both road and rail, perhaps we do need to look harder at cost effective tunnelling options, to reduce both visual intrusion and risk, and at more elegant noise reduction techniques.

We certainly have a need for engineering and design solutions which significantly raise environmental standards without significantly raising costs and, while that may sound like a tall order, it has to be a major objective.

Let me conclude then, by restating my opening remark. This is an attempt to define what the road user wants of the engineer, and that involves remembering conflicting objectives. There are some fairly specific requirements, which I have mentioned, and can now summarise, on Chart K.

The consumer in the transport field is badly in need of help.

Very high levels of personal mobility have in many cases become an absolute necessity – that is the concept of 'dependence'. But high levels of personal mobility are also a matter of choice, and preference, for the majority in today's society. Many of the things that people value and enjoy most are only accessible through personal mobility, and I cannot subscribe to a view that tells people they must forgo these things. At the same time consumers know there is an environmental problem arising from road transport. They perceive only dimly the true nature and extent of the problem, and they are often misled by the extremists. But they want the problems – whatever they are – to be solved.

The role of the engineer – of any description – is to use his or her professional integrity to help to give consumers the better environment they want, together with, not instead of, the freedom through personal mobility which they cherish.

# Session Three
# The Challenge
# for Transport

## Rapporteur

Alec Silverleaf CB FEng

## Personal Profile

**Alec Silverleaf** was educated at Kilburn Grammar School, London and the University of Glasgow (Department of Naval Architecture). He graduated with 1st Class honours in 1941. He joined William Denny & Bros. Shipbuilders having been a student apprentice (drawing and design office) with them during his time at University. He spent four years in the Research Department followed by five years as Head of the Ship Design Office.

In 1951 he moved to the National Physical Laboratory (NPL) at Teddington. He held various appointments over the next fourteen years and in 1965 was appointed Deputy Director responsible for the Engineering Sciences Group.

In 1971 Mr Silverleaf was appointed Director of the Transport and Road Research Laboratory (TRRL), a position he held until 1980 when he retired from UK Government service. Since then he has been involved with the International Transport Group (INTRA) as Co-ordinator and Co-founder. He also undertakes occasional technical advice functions in legal cases.

Mr Silverleaf was elected a Fellow of The Royal Academy of Engineering in 1980. He is a Foreign Member of The Royal Swedish Academy of Engineering Sciences, and an Honorary Fellow of the Institution of Highways and Transportation. He is a Fellow of The Royal Institution of Naval Architects, the Institution of Civil Engineers and the Chartered Institute of Transport.

# The Challenge for Transport

## Alec Silverleaf CB FEng

My task, as defined for me by our Chairman, has three parts. The first is to recall briefly some of the main points in the presentations we have just heard. Second, to place them in a broader context. Then third, to add some personal comments. So I begin by recalling the main points, or really messages, in the presentations.

Peter Hills concentrated on urban traffic problems and, in particular, on concepts of environmental capacity or space plus some broad questions about car use today and in the future. His main message was that a better balance can be obtained than we now have by a revival of transport planning coupled with traffic restraint, which he regards as unavoidable. The outlook for public transport he describes as bleak but he believes that greater use of telematics can improve traffic management provided, again, that there is a policy of traffic restraint.

Chris Elliott fortunately told us his message (it's not in his printed text). He said, "If you want Sustainable Development, listen to the engineers". My immediate reaction was "Oh no, *please*". I began my professional life as an engineer almost 60 years ago and since then I have steadily come to mistrust the judgement of engineers on such broad issues. However, in his printed paper he concentrated on how transport decisions are made, saying that they were often piecemeal, irrational and emotional. He gave us some elegant and challenging illustrations, and I suspect that they *will* be challenged. However, he gave us a positive message that a rational, comprehensive modelling approach can lead to better decisions about transport, and we need that if we are to achieve anything in the way of Sustainable Development.

David Worskett's message was, I think, fairly clear. Engineers, he tells us, should, and I suspect there is an element of 'must', help road users, whom he calls consumers, to have a better environment while retaining their freedom of personal mobility.

All three presentations had some common features. First, they all expect and accept continuing growth in transport. Second, they all confined their discussion essentially to local and national situations with very little about regional such as European or worldwide problems except for some of David Worskett's comparisons. But what they didn't say interests me as much as what they did. They say nothing, effectively, about air transport, which is of growing importance in any real Sustainable Development debate. They said little, if anything, about physical resources and their depletion, which is one of the central aspects of Sustainable Development. And they said very little indeed about social equity which is not unimportant in Sustainable Development arguments. Overall, it seemed to me that they were much more concerned with managing or containing development rather than in Sustainable Development, and I believe there to be a fundamental distinction between those two concepts.

Now let me try to put their views into a general context. Those of us who have worked in transport, and those who have thought about it, recognise that transport poses some very special problems for Sustainable Development. This is certainly so if the Brundtland type of definition is adopted, with its emphasis on inter-generational equity and its implications for social equity, or in plain English, fairness between rich and poor. It's even difficult if we adopt a more cynical approach and attitude leading to a more cynical, and perhaps more realistic definition, which can be put in many ways. One is "What I have I keep. If you can't pay you can't have the freedoms I have and you want". And a great deal of the Sustainable Development argument really has that at its core in spite of the splendid, idealistic things that Dame Rachel Waterhouse told us yesterday.

To begin with let's look back a little. The problems and anxieties which transport causes are far from new. In Imperial Rome there were restrictions on night movement of goods to reduce the noise of carts on its far from smooth urban roads. A century ago many cities in Western Europe feared that traffic, then almost entirely horsedrawn, would be brought to a halt by horse droppings and their anxiety reflected already very acute problems of urban congestion, probably worse then in some cities than those which afflict us now. So a sense of historical perspective is not a bad thing. But what is new is the severity and extent of these problems. What is also new is the adverse impact of transport on human lives. We have said very little about that here. Worldwide, every year more than a quarter of a million people are killed in transport accidents, more than three million are seriously injured, more than thirteen million are slightly injured. What is also new is the very severe adverse impact of transport on physical resources, not just energy, although that is extremely important, but on other material non-renewables. What is basically worrying is that transport will increase during the next decades. At the moment, worldwide, there are more than six hundred million road vehicles; five hundred million cars, a hundred million commercial vehicles plus another seventy five million two wheelers. Within two decades there will be double that number. I say will, not may. Most of that growth will occur outside OECD countries and it will not be halted by any pious resolutions on our part. There will be many people who are anxious to tap that market. So we have a situation in which it is not a question in transport of doing more with less, as we have heard so often, but of doing much more with not too much more. That is a very different situation, and certainly a very different one in terms of Sustainable Development.

I now venture some personal comments. I contend that what I have just said is a general context which does not reflect what I feel but what most of us recognise as being the real world in which we live. I believe that you can divide transport problems into two quite distinct groups, of quality and of quantity. We have heard a lot about the quality problems – noise, pollution, even fuel consumption, intrusive infrastructure, things of this kind. And we recognise that most of them are tractable and that they are being effectively tackled by engineers once they have been given the task. We have seen pollution levels due to road vehicles steadily decrease. Aircraft noise reduction is another good example.

But the other group, the quantity problems, are quite different. They remain, and we are doing little to control them. Large numbers of silent, pollution free stationary vehicles will still create intolerable congestion. Dealing with quality is necessary but it is far from sufficient. So how are we to tackle these questions of quantity? By restraint? Is that restraint to be voluntary or compulsory? Who is to be constrained? "I'm OK, you don't have it": is that what we mean by constraint? I said that initially in terms of rich and poor countries, but it's much wider. Peter Hills has long been an advocate of traffic constraint with road pricing as a necessary tool. But there are serious objections to almost all forms of road pricing. The problems of charging and of invasion of privacy may have been overcome, but others remain. A recent AA policy document said that road pricing, by whatever name it is disguised, or ecological tax reforms, all these are measures which "would bear most heavily on those least able to pay". I think we must recognise that any form of economic constraint runs counter to that kind of social equity about which some of us feel quite strongly.

What can engineers do? What should engineers do? I take an old fashioned view that engineering is primarily concerned with doing, with providing physical tools and creating physical artifacts. Providing those tools requires a great deal of intellectual effort. But there are no hard and fast distinctions, so that traffic engineering and transport planning are border-line activities, and engineering institutions are arguing whether those engaged in transport planning do qualify for membership. Engineers have already done a great deal in relation to transport and Sustainable Development. Take one example, a very important one. Engineers have been steadily reducing energy consumption on a unit vehicle basis. In many countries that reduction has averaged about one and a half per cent a year for the last 20 years. As a result of that and of possible further fuel efficiency improvements, future energy requirements for transport will be considerably reduced. Further, and perhaps equally important, saturation levels for the vehicle population will vary between countries depending on their economic circumstances. Overall, then, a very plausible forecast can be made that in the year 2030 worldwide energy requirements for transport will be no greater than the levels of the late 1970s in spite of the huge increase in the vehicle fleet. On the other hand there are equally plausible arguments which say that by the year 2030 transport will have greatly increased its energy consumption, and that crude oil will not be readily available for transport as there is a better market for it for petrochemicals. If there won't be very much left for us, the transport people, we had better start doing something about it now, though some folk are already doing so. What becomes clear is that sooner or later, and maybe sooner rather than later, we shall have to move towards something like hydrogen based fuels in spite of their inherent worries and difficulties, with, I suspect, some form of nuclear power generation to act as the driving force for those fuels. Transport is still the fastest growing end use sector of energy consumption and will remain so for the next 20 years. But when we talk about Sustainable Development we are concerned with more than 20 years ahead. So we have to think in those longer term perspectives of moving away from what are our staple sources of energy supply today for transport.

Finally, two general comments. The obstacles to real Sustainable Development are attitudes and the behaviour of individuals, this paradigm shift that we were told about yesterday. I take the view that engineers are no different from other citizens in that respect. They have no special skills or authority except those as thoughtful, knowledgeable, passionate citizens. So what are realistic objectives for transport in Sustainable Development? The Brundtland type definition is idealistic but unrealistic, and I would suggest that in the transport world the best that we can hope for is that engineers can help us to achieve a reduction of the adverse effects of transport, delay the depletion of non-renewable resources, and develop alternatives to present transport vehicles and systems. That's a pretty tall order, and engineers have quite a lot to contribute to achieving those objectives without worrying about idealism.

### Nigel Organ The Highways Agency

Would David Worskett comment on the implications of the trebling of the number of older drivers from about 5 million at the moment to about 15 million as the post war baby boom reaches retirement age? How will they maintain their mobility in some of the likely high tech solutions?

### David Worskett

I am not sure if the question is aimed at whether older people are going to be able to master in-car telematics. I have considerable confidence in their ultimate ability to do so. I think we are already seeing, and can measure, a higher level of dependence on the car amongst older people than in the past. As the proportion of elderly people in our society grows there will be more of them living in places which can't be adequately served by public transport. I think they are going to continue to be ever more dependent on their cars.

### Professor Sir Richard Southwood UK Round Table on Sustainable Development

Our last speaker ended by talking about attitudes and behaviour. When we take censuses or make attitudinal studies we need to know what is available and what is the actual environment in which we live and work. Part of the time I work in Budapest; now that the University has moved to a central site, even though I could still have a dedicated parking place, I take a tram because it is reliable and avoids the trouble of parking. In Oxford I also used a car and a dedicated parking place; now I find it quicker to cycle, though I may give this up for safety reasons. I have found that competing bus companies do not provide convenient services. There has been almost no mention of changing modes during a journey. Planning and engineering go together as part of the whole transport system. Will there be vehicles able to go from one mode to another?

### Professor Peter Hills

When I visited Budapest a few years ago car ownership was about one third that in the UK. They had an amazing tram system; very high frequencies, very highly subsidised. Obviously car ownership is now growing very fast in Eastern Europe and market pressures for their public transport to price properly must be very heavy. I fear that they will go the way that most Western countries go, ending up with very high car ownership and dwindling public transport support. On the question of your use of the car, I think on each occasion you said "with of course a dedicated parking place". Well, that's one of the problems. In most cities, 50%, if not more, of the car parking, particularly in central destinations, is private, non residential parking which is out of the control of local authorities. Unless we say this is an inducement for car use which we cannot allow to go on, and find a proper legal and, I hope, well reasoned way of bringing it under control, we simply have one hand tied behind our back in trying to restrain traffic in existing centres. Lastly, I know multi-modal transport is a great enthusiasm of yours. Again, I don't see this coming about on the scale needed to make an inroad on resource consumption without it being planned and at least pump primed with government or joint venture capital. The market is not going to bring this about. There simply is not enough incentive for it.

### Dr Chris Elliott

Three quick points. First the intermodal one. That really is what I understand to be behind the informed traveller outcome of Foresight. Secondly, the bus example is another case of a market free for all in which everybody loses. Thirdly, if engineers were handcuffed by market surveys, Henry Ford would never have got us into this position because the market wouldn't have wanted his cars. We have a duty as engineers, I am trying to argue, to present the options in an intelligent and understandable way, to present a good and bad side. We do not have to wait for the market to call for them.

### Alec Silverleaf

One of the great attractions of road transport, either by private car or commercial vehicle, is that it is the only single mode method. All the rest are intermodal, multi-modal methods, so one takes that for granted in discussions. Also, I suspect Mr Organ was talking about disadvantaged groups of people, not necessarily only the old. And for those, the kind of solution that David Worskett was suggesting won't work. You would be abandoning them if you do what he is suggesting and I don't think that a socially responsible British society will be prepared to abandon them to that extent. I may be wrong.

### Professor Anthony Kelly University of Cambridge

Two questions about inter-modal transport. Peter Hills said that without massive subsidy it won't occur. One of the advantages of travelling by car is that you can throw all your luggage into the boot without packing it. In Switzerland and in Holland, you can get out of a plane and take your luggage in a carrier directly to a train or bus. How was that introduced in Switzerland? And what is preventing the better integration of the modes of transport along the lines that Richard Southwood asked about?

### Professor Tony Ridley Chairman

A brief comment about Zurich. In Switzerland they have very high car ownership and very high use of public transport. Even, he says, the gnomes ride on trams in Zurich.

### David Worskett

One of the transport Foresight recommendations is the Clear Zone. Economically, and to a degree, practically, we have yet to crack what might loosely be termed the transhipment or integration problem. The Clear Zone concept endeavours to find ways in which you can have clean liveable town centres without delivery lorries, accessible only by clean forms of transport.

### Professor Peter Hills

Some points on Switzerland. First: I understand, bankers also go to work on the metro there; they are called metrognomes (laughter). Second, what one hears about seem to be attempts to ape, by public or at least collective transport, the extraordinary flexibility and convenience that private transport offers. To that extent they are still second best. You still have to wait for your very frequent, very flexible, public transport; you occasionally find yourself in inclement weather; and that the schedules don't work. Where they can compete and offer a service approaching that of private transport is in congested conditions. But they are very high cost precisely because they are aping private transport, and it is no surprise that this is done best in Switzerland where they have extremely high incomes, and a high willingness to pay for very high cost solutions. But it isn't just that. It also relies on a consensus, in the community's interest, on traffic restraint. It's beginning to emerge in other European countries like Sweden and Germany, but in the UK we have no basis as yet for a consensus that traffic restraint is in everybody's interest.

**Sara Parkin** Forum for the Future

There has been great emphasis on roads and cars. What engineers do is deliver services. With transport, surely the approach is not how do we get people mobile but how do we give people the access they need and how do we move around the things that make our society work? The freight problem is one of the most 'do-able'. Freight lorries on congested roads and busy motorways pose severe problems. We are an island with the possibility of moving freight by rail, on canals or by coastal shipping. Call me emotional or irrational, but if we think in system terms, as we must do, then these are not necessarily the constrained systems that Chris Elliott talked about. In biological sciences, systems are interlinked and quickly become 'global'. We should think about transport systems in that way. Would taking freight away from roads have great economic spinoffs?

## Alec Silverleaf

I wouldn't dream of calling you irrational but I would call you uneconomic because the policies you are suggesting would not be economically effective. When you buy any complicated piece of equipment – a car is a good example – it has been assembled in one place but its components have been made all over Europe at the very least. And they are shuttled to and fro by component manufacturers as directed by vehicle manufacturers. Who wants that? It is to meet *Just in Time* delivery methods coupled with dispersed production techniques which are highly economic because they use labour specialisms. When you can change that dominance of an industrial group, then you can begin to talk about changing modal split and reducing total transport 'performance' or movement.

## Sara Parkin

Surely the essence of the dilemma is getting the balance right between environmental economics and traditional economics; surely that has to be part of the discussion about how we deal with the transport problem?

## Alec Silverleaf

There is no such thing as 'we'. There are many self interest groups who don't have anything in common. So you have to change those dominant groups, not just the people who are ready to respond to your views, but those who are totally unready and unwilling.

## Dr Chris Elliott

Any company which at the moment decided to ship its goods by canal would lose financially. People accused me this morning of being dispassionate. Accountants are substantially worse. They choose the cheapest route. If we are going to follow what you say we have to look at it on a much larger scale.

## David Worskett

There is nothing the car driver would like more than to see these lorries off the roads. But we must distinguish between long distance and shorter distance: the economics of putting long distance freight on to railway, using combined transport and the like, are getting better and more plausible. Even if you did that it's barely a pinprick on the total volume of freight moving around; a huge amount is effectively local distribution. You cannot take a railway line into every supermarket in order to give them their *Just in Time* deliveries.

## Professor Peter Hills

The important thing we should do is make road freight pay the full marginal cost at the point of use of the road space. That would make a more level playing field between modes, but sadly I fear that road freight would still be dominant. But the point is that door to door road freight, rather like private transport, is very flexible and convenient and people are increasingly willing to pay for that. Increasingly road freight is concentrating on motorways, and the existing infrastructure can handle the growth in road freight. The problem is the potential growth in car traffic.

### Sir William Barlow

The fashion for *Just in Time* started by the Japanese car companies and followed by much of industry, puts a large amount of extra underloaded freight traffic on the roads. You get the case where some items are delivered every hour, some every two hours, some twice a day. Now, instead of large numbers of regional distribution centres which most companies used to have, the move is to have large ones at motorway intersections, increasing the mileage on the roads. My own former company had distribution warehouses all over the country in every major city. Now it has three or four. Because motorway usage is free to commercial users, they are going increasingly for large distribution centres. The whole system of distribution now is putting extra commercial vehicles on the road and they do it without paying the cost they incur.

### Professor Peter Hills

The point is that heavy road vehicles are not paying the full costs at the point of use and one effect of a motorway tolling system would be to reduce journey lengths. It would begin to reverse the warehousing process you have described as well as reducing car journey lengths. That would ease traffic flows on motorways, not hugely but perceptibly.

To alter a pricing regime sets in train many consequential changes. Economic theory tells us, and as engineers we should be on top of economic theory in this respect, that efficient pricing, which is charging the full costs at the point of use, is better than inefficient charging and produces a benefit which we can then allocate in many different ways. Merely shifting fixed tax on to a pay as you go charge, whose revenue total is the same, will produce efficiency gains and we really ought not play that down.

### Rear Admiral William Rourke Australian Academy of Technical Sciences and Engineering

Although the geography of Japan is admittedly different we should all be aware that the Japanese Ministry of Transport is planning a massive modal shift of their lorry traffic off their roads, which they say cannot sustain the operation in a way that is environmentally sound. They are planning to move a very large proportion of their freight traffic on to rail which carries only a very small proportion at the moment and on to fast sea transport. There is general, broad acceptance that sustainability and environmental requirements in Japan require that massive shift from the roads to sea and rail.

### Donald Bruce Church of Scotland

All these predictions of growth of transport are to some extent self fulfilling prophecies so that if you have a certain prediction for a growth of so much transport then you will build the infrastructure, no matter what sort of transport it is. If on the other hand you said, "Do we actually need all this increased mobility?" you might find you didn't need it as much as you thought. One of the fundamental underlying questions is, "Are there ways that we can remove this inevitability that we have become so utterly dependent" as Mr Worskett said, "on more mobility for freight, for passengers and so forth?" – surely there must be some point at which mobility stops?

### David Worskett

It really is back to the fundamental point of what it is we are trying to manage. It seems to me the real point is whether or not one does accept the thesis that a large part of car use, probably freight as well, is just derived from the overall structural nature of our society, our lifestyles, our economic requirements and the like. If it is, then we have a very big issue indeed – inviting people to change lifestyles quite fundamentally. I am quite confident about our ability to change attitudes and behaviour on what one might call micro issues; we succeeded very effectively on something like drinking and driving. I am far far less sanguine about asking for a major change in structures and lifestyles across a whole range of activities, which is what you would have to do to attack the problem in the way which is being suggested. I don't really believe that much of this mobility is happening purely spuriously. I think it is driven by real attachment, either need or genuine attachment and personal preference for a particular lifestyle.

### Professor Peter Hills

The Department of Transport produced national traffic forecasts in 1984 which were based on not very rapidly rising car ownership up to then; because it was essentially an extrapolatory model it forecast not very great increases. The surge in car ownership in the late '80s, was consistently above the high forecast. So in 1989 they revised the national forecasts and came up with the much quoted low estimate of 89% more, and a high estimate of 143% more. Shock horror! Everybody asked "how on earth does the Department of Transport expect us to accommodate all this traffic?" But it arises from people buying cars. And if you say this is self fulfilling we have to ask ourselves why all of us have a car (or two or three) in our households and say "isn't it a perfectly reasonable aspiration for people who don't yet have the level of income to attain this?" It provides the reason why a doubling of traffic between now and 2025, on present policies and with present attitudes, is not fanciful. And if we really can't face this sustainably then we have to do a lot of the things that I was trying to say.

### Dr Elizabeth Ness BICC Cables

The company to which your President referred now has only two warehouses. We are a pan-European and global company. Our customers are pan-European and we are seeing a tension between the free movement of goods ethic, the requirements of the single market, and the demands which freight transport places on the communities through which it travels.

### Nick Cooke British Nuclear Fuels plc

Is not safety an emotive issue which as a society we deal with in an irrational way? We have a media that highlights air and coach incidents and underplays the toll on the roads. As a result we expect higher standards of safety in public transport than we expect in private transport. We as engineers should not just be analysing and coming up with solutions; there is also an enormous job to do in presenting those solutions and explaining to the public again and again.

### Professor Roland Clift University of Surrey

I want to come back to a point which seems to me to be important and to have been lost. The future of transport is 'how do you do a very great deal more with not too much more?' That means how do you resource it and in particular how do you power it, where does the energy come from? I am delighted that no-one has mentioned bio diesel. If you look at the distances over which very simple foodstuffs are transported, and the energy costs of so doing, then a simple calculation says, if instead of growing bio diesel on set-aside land we grew carrots and ate them locally, you end up a very long way ahead. The sustainable future has to be local production, not transported.

### Professor Peter Hills

There are misperceptions of safety which are of concern. Since the King's Cross disaster a huge amount has been invested in safety measures. Double exits are now required from all the stations on the Jubilee line extension so adding a huge cost simply deriving from a very serious over estimation of the value of avoiding a low probability risk. This is in contrast with a very much higher risk of similar accidents happening on private transport. One of the things we could do is to expose the facts about the relative risks and the economic worth of insuring against them. My other point is about freight transport. Road freight movements which lead to conflicts with local communities can be dealt with by a form of traffic calming. Heavy vehicles are prevented from invading local environments – as is done on the Continent – and made to use main roads and to accept any extra costs.

### Dr Chris Elliott

Our duty as engineers is to do the calculations, to present the arguments showing that if you do grow carrots locally it's better than moving them. Then we can take rational decisions.

### David Worskett

If the local community is being damaged by freight on a strategic route, then build a by-pass in the most environmentally sensitive way you can, but build it. Yes, the safety debate is often irrational. But you have only to look at how the UK has become one of the two best countries in the world in terms of its road safety record. The principal reason is that we analysed the causes of accidents properly, we quantified them, we prioritised them, and we looked to engineers as professionals for specific solutions to specific types of accidents.

### Alec Silverleaf

Individual actions are very little influenced by major dramatic transport events. An air accident does not have any impact on air travel, but if I buy a ticket as a customer on public transport I expect to be protected more than when I use my car at my own risk. Secondly, growing carrots locally in a de-regulated free market – how are we going to do that? Thirdly, the motives for buying cars and using commercial vehicles are not related to forecasts. When I buy a car I don't say "the forecast says there will be a lot more of us". I just want a car, and incidentally when I buy a car I am a consumer, when my neighbour buys a car I'm a voter.

### Chairman

Ladies and gentlemen, it's been said many many times, that transport is a derived demand. I begin to reflect that transport engineering is a derived profession. What we do, what we can do, depends on whether we have free markets or not, on decisions made by Ministers and local government officials about the location of hospitals, schools etc. We are not capable of handling this issue on our own. Engineers do things: that ought to be the central driving force of the engineer's contribution. But, of course, engineers want to do the right things if they can decide properly what the right things are. We have to define the objectives or someone has to define them for us. What are we trying to achieve in transport or how do we find what society wants to achieve? Even today, in this august body we are not entirely sure in a single minded fashion what it is we are all about.

THE ROYAL ACADEMY OF ENGINEERING

# Engineering for Sustainable Development

## SESSION FOUR

### Issues for Engineers

**Chairman**  Sir Martin Holdgate CB
**Rapporteur**  Dr James McQuaid FEng

**Panellists**

Lord Tombs of Brailes FEng

Dr Robert Frosch FEng

Sir John Knill FEng

Sara Parkin

# Session Four
# Issues for
# Engineers

## Chairman

Sir Martin Holdgate CB

Chairman, Energy Advisory Panel,
Department of Trade and Industry

## Personal Profile

**Sir Martin Holdgate** graduated in zoology and botany from Cambridge University in 1952 and after completing his PhD three years later began a period of research on the ecology and biogeography of Antarctic and sub Antarctic regions. Between 1955 and 1964 he divided his time between teaching in the Universities of Manchester, Durham and Cambridge, and field studies in the Tristan da Cunha islands, the southernmost parts of Chile, and the maritime Antarctic regions. After four years as Deputy Director of the Nature Conservancy, Sir Martin entered central Government as the first Director of the Central Unit on Environmental Pollution, and between 1970 and 1988 he served successively as Chief Scientist in the Departments of the Environment and Transport and as Deputy Secretary (Environment Protection) in DOE. During that period he lead numerous UK delegations to international environmental meetings, and served as the President of the Governing Council of the UN Environment Programme in 1983-84. He left the Civil Service in 1988 to become Director General of IUCN – The World Conservation Union, which has its headquarters near Geneva and is the world's largest association of Governmental and Non-Governmental organizations concerned with the conservation and sustainable use of natural resources.

Sir Martin retired from IUCN in April 1994 and was knighted in June that year. Among other activities, he is currently Rapporteur of the UN High Level Advisory Board on Sustainable Development, President of the Zoological Society of London, Chairman of the International Institute for Environment and Development, and a member of the Royal Commission on Environmental Pollution.

# Issues for Engineers

## Sir Martin Holdgate CB

In round terms, this must be about the fiftieth Conference on Sustainable Development that I have attended. In one sense, this may be encouraging. It shows that the importance of the subject is widely recognized. On the other hand, one worries about the value added by each meeting when so many rehearse the same arguments. So what is special about this Conference? I think the answer is that it is a serious attempt to examine how one of the professions with most to contribute should help to build a sustainable future for society, here in the United Kingdom and around the world.

Like other Conferences, this one began by reminding all of us of the basic definitions. *Development* is defined in the Oxford Dictionary as "slow unfolding: gradual working out". It is the process by which humanity, over prehistory and history, has transformed the natural world so that our species has become pan-dominant. The success of development is demonstrated by the fact that the Earth today sustains more people than ever before, and that the standard of living of most of them has been rising steadily.

But development has not been a universal success. Its dark side has been land degradation, pollution, squalid shanty towns on the fringes of many great cities, millions suffering from persistent poverty, malnutrition and avoidable disease, and millions more enduring a mix of unemployment and poor living that erodes human dignity.

This is the foundation for the environmental challenge. For it is clear that our use of natural resources has been profligate. Humanity today – with around 5.8 billion people on Earth – is said to pre-empt, use or waste about 39% of the net primary production (the fixation of carbon and energy by green plants) on land. We cannot expect to double that appropriation as we move to a future where there may be twice as many people to feed. There will have to be greater efficiency.

Sustainable Development has been hailed as the recipe for that enhanced efficiency, so we meet human needs better and "meet the needs of the present without compromising the ability of future generations to meet their own needs". The World Commission on Environment and Development that coined the phrase (WCED, 1987) made it clear that they saw social change as the key to sustainable development, allowing better management of the environment so that it could deliver more of what people required, today and tomorrow. Allowing – to quote Sir Robin Ibbs' remarks to this Conference – society to have its cake and eat it.

## Achieving Sustainable Development

Agenda 21, the great 40-Chapter action plan for the 21st century adopted at the UN Conference on Environment and Development in Rio de Janeiro in June 1992, emphasizes that Sustainable Development cannot be achieved by the United Nations alone, or governments alone, or green environmentalists alone (Robinson, 1993; UN, 1993). It demands synergy between all sectors of society and all nations. Engineers and other professionals are rightly identified as important contributors. The private sector of business, industry and commerce is recognized as a principal engine of change in a world where market economies are dominant and private sector investment moves about twenty times as much money into the developing countries as does government-to-government aid.

But *how* can Sustainable Development be achieved? There are some assumptions in the concept that gloss over real political difficulties. Is inter-community equity really achievable in a competitive world? Does restraint in the name of inter-generational equity make economic sense given the steady increase in human intellectual and technical skills? (Wilfred Beckerman argued in 1994 that it does not). Can the market deliver sustainability, or must limits be imposed on its operation – for example to prevent unacceptable pollution, climate change and resource degradation? But how can such constraints on the market themselves be made equitable, avoiding barriers to trade in the products of communities and countries that need to develop economically and preventing disadvantage to countries and companies that set high environmental standards in the name of sustainable development? Do we need to turn GATT into GATTE – the General Agreement on Tariffs, Trade and the Environment? The World Trade Organization is beginning to grapple with this question.

The Business Council for Sustainable Development (Schmidheiny, 1992) argued that the key for industry lay in *ecoefficiency* – efficiency in the use of raw materials and energy, low or no waste, zero pollution *and* high productivity and competitiveness. Splendid. We know that it can be done, and in this Conference Sir Ronald Hampel, Dr Ziebart, Dr White and others have illustrated how the best firms can do it. But how general is best practice – how can the global paradigm, in Professor Roland Clift's terms, be shifted?

Can engineers shift the paradigm? Sir William Barlow, in his Presidential message reminded us that "there has been a lack of consistent engineering thrust in the Sustainable Development debate thus far". Yet the building of a sustainable society is a task to which engineers must contribute. By 2050 over 75% of the world population will live in cities. They will depend for the necessities and opportunities of life on the built fabric, the transport system and the social infrastructure that operates both. Engineers must be active in helping to define the goals for tomorrow's societies because you construct their physical fabric. You must develop and apply engineering ecoefficiency. Dame Rachel Waterhouse made this point very clearly. For just as the structure of the market channels economic enterprise, so the structure of the city channels how citizens can live. The engineer is upstream of the consumer, but needs to work downstream of the articulation of social needs.

One thing that has struck me over the past 23 years as we moved from the UN Conference on the Human Environment in Stockholm in 1972 to the UN Conference on Environment and Development in Rio in 1992 has been the relative invisibility of the world of business – and of engineering. Of course there were two World Industry Conferences on Environmental Management (Sallada and Doyle, 1986: Willums, 1991). The Business Council for Sustainable Development made an important contribution to the Earth Summit in Rio (Schmidheiny, 1992). The International Chamber of Commerce has published a Business Charter for Sustainable Development (Willums and Golucke, 1992). But my general impression is that engineers, once hailed as the heroic builders of the industrial world, recoiled in shock when the environmental attack began and although they have re-grouped, with the rest of industry, and done much to help achieve Sustainable Development they have remained too much in a responsive, almost apologetic, mode. I ask the Royal Academy and this Conference to consider the need for more visible leadership in developing and promoting the practical solutions Sir William Barlow spoke of yesterday. Joan Ruddock said that engineers lacked identity as creators of Sustainable Development. You need to recover that leadership.

## The Conclusions of the Sessions

There is clearly a need for forecasting. Engineers create structures and products, many of which have an intended life span of decades or even centuries. Even short-lived consumer goods have long design times. Forecasting the expectations of society – the theme of Session One of this Conference – is a necessity. The President of the Board of Trade spoke of *Technology Foresight* and the need for Government to provide an enabling framework. The discussion after Joan Ruddock's paper picked up some of its elements – especially the need to note the value judgements of society as well as to evaluate more objectively the sensitivity of the environment and the impact of products and processes upon it. Dame Rachel Waterhouse emphasized the same need when she said "technological development – however imaginative and inspired – will not get very far unless it is in step with consumer needs, aspirations and concerns". People need to be able to make informed choices about the new developments in society – from mega schemes like tidal barrages to the micro-level of household consumables –but designers of chemical, electrical, mechanical and civil engineering products also need to make informed judgements about what to create that will meet social and environmental needs and this means blending forecasting with risk assessment and, as the Bishop of Oxford said, with the precautionary principle. Engineers cannot do this alone: you need dialogue with environmental and social scientists. And we all need to recognize in this context – again referring to the Bishop of Oxford – that the environment provides spiritual and inspirational support as well as products. Tropical forests, to quote the title of a paper by Norman Myers (1988) are much more than logs of wood. We need that wide-ranging dialogue across all sectors of society for which Agenda 21 called. That in turn can lead to the targets that the Bishop of Oxford and Professor Kelly called for, and perhaps remove the more destructive impacts of the adversarial debate we worried over in discussion.

Sustainable Development is about equity. As the Bishop of Oxford stressed, there is a moral imperative for economic growth in the developing world. All our efforts to achieve clean technology here will be of no avail if that development does not use best technology. There is an immense challenge to get best practices adopted world wide. But this could mean transferring to competitors the knowledge gained at the cost of much research. One good way forward could be for the most advanced firms to recognize the potential markets in the developing world and take their products and processes there. But for this to happen there has to be a convergence of vision and values between different countries and communities –and the world system needs to ensure that inward investment is not impeded by bad governance or barriers to the derivation of profits. It seems to me that a major goal of official development aid should be the creation of infrastructure in developing counties – the framework of law and fiscal policy, education, and good administration – which in turn encourages inward private sector investments and the technology essential for sustainable development.

The second session gave us encouraging examples of advances towards ecoefficiency. ICI and BMW are clearly responding to social demand and are providing products that will help solve major environmental problems. They are not alone – I am sure that Dow or DuPont would provide matching illustrations and only three weeks ago I heard Percy Barnevik, Chief Executive Officer of ASEA Brown Boveri, give a striking address on the same topics within the energy generation and transmission fields. Sir Ronald Hampel listed the steps that a company must take internally to establish environmental awareness and commitment – and this clearly has to start at the top with the Chief Executive and the Main Board, and extend through the whole culture of the company. Sir Ronald also set out seven wider conditions for sustainable development – again addressing the governance and the economic context and linking back to points made by Mr Lang.

Peter White gave us a good picture of how life cycle assessment can contribute to defining, and so reducing, environmental impact. You may recall the 'epitaph' coined by some wit for that monumental architect, Sir John Vanbrugh:

> *Lie heavy on him, Earth – for he*
> *Laid many a heavy load on thee!*

Life cycle inventories are designed to lighten the load industry places on the Earth and on its environmental systems – which are our life support system.

Roland Clift gave us a lively, imaginative set of conclusions. We can and must satisfy more human needs from less energy and materials, and with much less pollution and waste. We must try to switch from non-renewable to renewable resources, used sustainably. Engineers must engage in the public debate (a chorus refrain heard through the whole two days).

Transport is crucial in any modern society. Urbanization cuts people off from the hinterland from which cities get their food. As Professor Ridley said, economic growth depends on efficient transport, yet transport is condemned as a principal destroyer of the environment. Peter Hills and David Worskett pointed up the familiar paradox: that whatever we say against it, road and especially car transport is inescapably central to the foreseeable future. As Alec Silverleaf repeated: the solution may come through a better balance, achieved through planning and traffic restraint.

Christopher Elliott gave some telling comparisons of energy efficiency which run counter to much intuitive public judgement. An Oxford electric bus is just as polluting as a diesel minibus, but the pollution is transferred to Didcot. A TGV is not much different to a jet aircraft in energy efficiency terms. There may be no rational engineering or environmental case for electric vehicles or trains. Does logical engineering analysis lead towards a quite new kind of vehicle? Or are the models wrong because the wrong costs and values – especially environmental costs and values – have been fed into them? Should we accept the rationality of irrationality – of people's feelings? David Worskett argued that the use of road vehicles in OECD countries today is not only rational, but made more so by changing employment patterns which in turn demand higher personal mobility.

I would add here that we should not close our eyes to the fact that in most developing countries road transport networks dominate, and will continue to dominate. I doubt if anybody will build new railroads, apart from urban metro systems. Hence the sustainable car and the sustainable lorry on the sustainable road must be the goal, and we cannot expect a standstill to the development of any of these. As Alec Silverleaf commented, the challenge is to do much more with not too much more – paying attention to the qualities and quantities of action and impact.

## Conclusions: Actions for Engineers

Eight general points strike me as important as we move forward.

*First*, speak louder. Nobody can hear you. This meeting has heard many encouraging stories of progress towards environmental compatibility: towards not just end-of-pipe solutions but radical re-design to give processes and products that are profitable, efficient, meet social needs and safeguard the environment. We could have multiplied the examples many times over. But they have not got across to the public. As Dame Rachel Waterhouse said, "the distinctive contribution of engineers needs to be sold, not just at gatherings like this one". The Bishop of Oxford spoke of communication as a key aspect of the engineer's role today. As he said, the human capacity to solve problems exists, if the will is there. The will for Sustainable Development *is* there. What is lacking is the awareness that it can be delivered in practical form at an acceptable price. The engineering world knows that it can be. But there are few signs of leadership. You need to turn outwards and publicize your achievements, and by reinforcing the public demand for good, sustainable engineering you will also reinforce the standing of your own profession. Engage in the debate!

*Second*, go on developing the *Code of Conduct* and *Guide on Environmental Issues*. As before, do it in dialogue with environmentalists like Sara Parkin. But do not stop at an internal document. Spread it around. Put it into the Round Table on Sustainable Development. Amplify it as a contribution to local Agenda 21s and the National Strategy for Sustainable Development. But all this is inadequate if it is confined to the United Kingdom. Make common cause with the other academies of engineering in the European Union. Engage in the wider debate!

*Third*, take seriously Professor Roland Clift's challenge to move energy and material flows from the non-renewable to the renewable side of the system. But there is another, linked, opportunity here. I urge you to work with nature and enlist the powers of natural engineering. Nature can do, and does, much for free. Bacterial degradation, after all, is the heart of sewage and much organic waste treatment. It can be enhanced. Salt marshes, dunes, mangrove forests and coral reefs provide millions of dollars worth of coast protection – and their value is often only appreciated when they are destroyed and expensive human engineered solutions become necessary. The right kind of vegetation provides free reinforced earth. Should not bioengineering be a growth industry – an alliance between ecologists, who know the optimum conditions for micro-organisms, plants and animals, and engineers who can create or enhance them?

*Fourth*, recognize that environmental technology is itself big business – we heard estimates of around \$200 billion rising to \$500 billion. Recognize that environmental and social demands are universal arbiters and will make more stringent demands. The Royal Commission on Environmental Pollution (1984) coined the term 'Best Practicable Environmental Option' or BPEO, to describe a choice which optimized the impact of a discharge or waste disposal route between air, water, land and sea rather than treating these as separate compartments. BPEO, like BATNEEC, also has a cost dimension. But the Brent Spar episode and others like it have demonstrated that a scientific, technical and economic assessment may not suffice. BPEO has to become BESPO – best environmentally and socially practicable option. Product assessment likewise needs to take the social choice element aboard. Again, dialogue with those outside the world of engineering is the best way of alerting engineers to the way social expectations may move and enhancing the information available to the people making the choices. Sir Ronald Hampel rubbed the point in – and once again it comes back to the refrain: 'participate in the debate'.

Professor Roland Clift's summary of Session 2 led me to note two further points: do not take public rationality for granted, and recognize that the road is littered with corpses in the form of left-overs from past decisions. The paradigm shift to Sustainable Development may be guiding decisions now, but there are many relics of past unsustainable action that loom large in public concern and demand remedy. And while the paradigm may have shifted here, there are still many parts of the world where it has not.

*Fifth*, recognize that Sustainable Development is built from the ground up (something that all the global generalization and waffle can easily obscure). Nobody can engineer the global ecosystem into new balance. We can only address its components, working to solve problems and applying the solutions progressively. The ozone hole can only be filled by introducing effective substitutes for CFCs – and waiting fifty years for the CFCs now in the atmosphere to be destroyed. Solving oxidant smog means getting $NO_x$ and hydrocarbon concentrations down, and this means clean cars (among other things). Sustainable Development means practical innovation – and life cycle assessment is relevant here. As Dr Elliott pointed out, an electric car does not necessarily have a lighter environmental footprint than a diesel: it simply treads elsewhere on the Earth. Engineers, as Sir Robin Ibbs said, are good at practical solutions: at practical judgements and at balancing risks. We need to accelerate practical innovation that responds to well-diagnosed needs. Sustainable Development, to quote Stewart Miller, is compatible with economic growth. As the second World Conservation Strategy (IUCN/UNEP/WWF, 1991) says, "it can be done without rejecting the many benefits that modern technology has brought, provided that technology works within those limits". But as Professor Kelly said, for this to happen practical solutions must focus on defined targets. And those targets will be set for long-term human welfare –for Health, Safety and Environment.

*Sixth*, press Governments to do as the President of the Board of Trade said, and create the framework – legal, regulatory, economic and political – in which industry can build with confidence. We take this for granted here, but as I said earlier, governance remains a factor limiting investment in much of the developing world. Helping to build world economic and political stability should be seen by governments as a principal task of the United Nations. Peace building is as important as – or more important than – peace keeping.

*Seventh*, remember the dinosaurs. Evolution is the result of creativity and diversification on the one hand and selection, with extinction of the uncompetitive, on the other. Some life forms – like crocodiles – can hang on for a long time because they are highly successful in a specialized niche that nothing else seems to want to challenge. Others, like the Giant Panda, appear doomed because their niche is contracting and their design is illogical: bears are not built to live largely on bamboo shoots. Reviewing our transport debate, Alec Silverleaf emphasized the need for a wider historical and social perspective. The debate left me with this conundrum: have we an illogical system because we have constrained its evolutionary ecology (or, in non-biological terms, interfered in the market, distorted inter-modal competition and imposed social judgements which have led to the wrong system)? Or must society intervene in the market because the market alone will not create the social optimum? Dr Elliott posed the question: can we create adequate transport systems without looking at the anatomy of the sustainable city? Socially, can we create the conditions for evolution of engineered products that meet social needs and are flexible and adaptive?

*Eighth* and finally, I think we come back to the properties of complex systems. The enviro-socio-econo-techno-system is complex: so are the world's climatic and ecological systems. World climate models are notoriously difficult to build, and the problems of modelling the social and environmental system were underlined in the 1970s by the Club of Rome Report *Limits to Growth* (Meadows et al, 1972). In this Conference we have seen the problems of modelling even smaller components like the transport system. Engineers understand complex systems, but also how to get to pragmatic solutions that work. As was said in this Conference there is something of a cultural division here between mathematicians and physical scientists on the one hand, who grapple with uncertainty, and engineers who cut their way through by approximation (termed by the vulgar 'fudge factors'). Sustainable Development demands practical advances that start from where we are now and provide realistic solutions to the problems we can define – while allowing a safety margin for uncertainty and a capacity to adapt. I believe that you, as engineers, have the mind set – the paradigm – to respond, and I trust that you will get on with the practical process of building Sustainable Development, demonstrating that it can work, telling people what you are doing and so making it clear to everyone that engineers can deliver what the world needs. Good luck!

## References

Beckerman, W. (1995) *Small is Stupid. Blowing the Whistle on the Greens.* London: Duckworth.

IUCN/UNEP/WWF (1991) *Caring for the Earth. A Strategy for Sustainable Living.* Gland, Switzerland: International Union for Conservation of Nature and Natural Resources.

Meadows, D.H., Meadows, D.L. Randers, J and Behrens, W.W. (1972) *The Limits to Growth.* New York: Universe.

Myers, N. (1988) *Tropical Forests: Much more than Stocks of Wood. Journal of Tropical Ecology,* 4, 1-13.

RCEP (1984) *Tackling Pollution – Experience and Prospects. Tenth Report of the Royal Commission on Environmental Pollution.* London: HMSO.

Robinson, N. (Ed) (1993) *Agenda 21: Earth's Action Plan* New York, London, Rome: Oceana Publications.

Sallada, L. H. and Doyle, B. G. (Eds) (1986) *The Spirit of Versailles: The Business of Environmental Management.* Report of the First World Industry Conference on Environmental Management. Paris: ICC Publishing SA.

Schmidheiny, S. (1992) *Changing Course: A Global Business Perspective on Development and the Environment.* Cambridge, Mass: MIT Publications.

UN (1993) *Report of the United Nations Conference on Environment and Development.* New York: United Nations Publications, Sales No. E.93.I.8.

WCED (1987) *Our Common Future.* Oxford: University Press.

Willums, J.-O. (Ed) (1991) *WICEM II Conference Report and Background Papers.* Paris: ICC Publications.

Willums, J.-O. and Golucke, U. (1992) *From Ideas to Action. Business and Sustainable Development. The ICC Report on the Greening of Enterprise 1992.* Oslo, Norway: ICC and Ad Notam Gyldendal.

# Session Four

## Issues for Engineers

### Chairman

Sir Martin Holdgate CB

Chairman, Energy Advisory Panel,
Department of Trade and Industry

### Panellists

**Lord Tombs of Brailes FEng** was Chairman of Rolls-Royce from 1985 to 1992. He spent much of his career in the electricity industry, rising to become Chairman of the South of Scotland Electricity Board (1969-77) and Chairman of the Electricity Council (1977-80). He was Chairman of the Weir Group (1981-83) and of Turner and Newall (renamed T&N) (1982-89). Lord Tombs was a member of the Nature Conservancy Council 1978-82; the Standing Committee on Energy and the Environment (1978) and the Science and Engineering Research Council (1982-85). He was Chairman of the Engineering Council (1985-88); ACARD (1985-87) and ACOST (1987-90). He is currently Chairman of the House of Lords Select Committee on Sustainable Development.

Lord Tombs is a Past President of the Institution of Electrical Engineers (1981-82). He is an Honorary Fellow of the Institutions of Chemical, Electrical, Civil, Production and Mechanical Engineers. He was Pro-Chancellor and Chairman of the Council of Cranfield Institute of Technology (1985-91) and is currently Chancellor of Strathclyde University.

**Dr Robert Frosch FEng** is currently Senior Research Fellow and Adjunct Lecturer at the Centre for Science and International Affairs, John F. Kennedy School of Government, Harvard University. He was formerly Vice President of General Motors, Administrator of the National Aeronautics and Space Administration (NASA), and Assistant Secretary of the Navy for Research and Development. He has provided technical leadership at the highest level in the fields of oceanography, naval science and engineering, space technology and automotive engineering. He is Senior Fellow of the US National Academy of Engineering and a Foreign Member of The Royal Academy of Engineering.

**cont.**

**Sir John Knill FEng** is a Director of Donaldson Associates Ltd, which specialises in the design and supervision of tunnel construction. He was the Chairman and Chief Executive of the Natural Environment Research Council for five years until 1993.

He is a geologist, having worked particularly in the application of geology in the civil engineering industry and in relation to environmental issues. He joined Imperial College in 1957 where he developed teaching and research in engineering geology becoming Professor in 1973 and then Head of the Department of Geology and Dean of the Royal School of Mines. His professional interests have been largely concerned with the application of geology in heavy construction such as dams, reservoirs, slopes and tunnels, in waste management, in natural hazard assessment and in the engineering aspects of quarries and mines. He has travelled throughout the world as a consultant dealing with such matters.

He has considerable interests in the role of the earth sciences within the environment and conservation and is Chairman of the UK's Co-ordinating Committee on the International Decade of Natural Disaster Reduction, was a member of the Nature Conservancy Council and is now one of the three independent scientists on the Joint Nature Conservation Committee.

**Sara Parkin** is one of Britain's leading writers and campaigners on environmental issues. For over 20 years she has been closely involved with the development of green politics worldwide, serving at various times as Chair of the UK Green Party and Co-secretary of the European Greens, and lecturing and advising on many aspects of environmental policy for a wide variety of audiences, including NATO's Senior Officer College. She is a Trustee of the New Economics Foundation.

Her connections with the engineering profession go back to 1990, and she has worked with The Engineering Council on the development of their *Code of Professional Practice and Guidelines on Environmental Issues.*

Currently she is a Director of Forum for the Future, a new charity established by leading UK environmentalists to take a positive solution-oriented approach to building a sustainable way of life. In particular she is preparing a scholarship programme for young people and establishing a best practice for sustainability database.

She is author of many Green Party programmes and several books, including *Green Parties: An International Guide* (Heretic, 1989) and *The Life and Death of Petra Kelly* (Pandora, 1994).

### Sir Martin Holdgate CB Chairman

We will begin with observations from the panel, then take submitted questions and then questions from the floor.

### Lord Tombs of Brailes FEng

Can I begin by making some generalised comments on the question of Sustainable Development which stem from the work of the House of Lords Select Committee over the past 15 months. The first is that the scientific base on which much of the need for measures to achieve Sustainable Development are based is very shaky. If you take, for example, climate prediction: first of all the model is not complete and secondly the data series is really quite short. If you take the question of biodiversity, there are many micro organisms not even recognised as yet. Also I may add that we don't understand many of the atmospheric mechanisms for conversion, for example nitrogenous oxides. The method of costing environmental issues is equally shaky in its basis as the scientific one. There are, of course, protagonists who would argue differently, Professor Pearce leads them. He believes you can attach a meaningful value to a countryside view for example, which I think is going rather a long way. Of course, absence of firm data doesn't preclude the need for action. Externalities will inevitably come to be included in costs, if steps are taken towards a more sustainable environment. They may be shaky, they may be judgements initially but they will have to appear. The inadequacy of the scientific and economic bases actually increases the scope for political judgement, which is a bad thing, so it is essential that we try to remedy those deficiencies as quickly as we can. On the Conference so far: first, the plea for rational analysis of everything. I am all in favour if it could be done. Of course it can't be done in quite the way we might wish it to be done. It can't be done because we have imperfect knowledge and we are dealing with the future. As Groucho Marx has said "you should never predict anything, especially the future". I think some of the biggest mistakes of my life were made after the most extensive and well-informed analysis possible and I quote two examples , one I had something to do with, the other I had nothing to do with. Energy forecasts have been wrong again and again in a most spectacular way. The Three Mile Island accident came after decades of experience of safety analysis on light water reactors and it turned out that the continuous small leak had never been examined. And that's what happened at Three Mile Island. So we should approach this question of rational decisions with a degree of humility. Our knowledge is, by its very nature, incomplete because we haven't lived through the future yet. Also we have (as Alec Silverleaf has drawn out) to deal with people and people are a further complication with which engineers are not peculiarly well equipped to deal. There is clearly going to be a need for a change in the lifestyle of the Western world and certainly in this country and in others in Europe the will is visible in the way that people respond, for example, to recycling campaigns with domestic refuse, with the use of smaller cars or diesel cars. So there is a will there and that will needs to be reinforced and led because people are entitled to leadership and need it accelerated by fiscal and regulatory measures. We have not been very good at that so far.

The final point I want to deal with is that of social equity, the notion that, for example, motorway tolls would bear more heavily on the poor than on the rich. Now this isn't a problem that is peculiar to Sustainable Development. But I have no doubt that the way in which social questions of that kind have to be tackled is by political means, through taxes and the welfare system. You can't take just Sustainable Development and say we won't have any inequalities. Inequalities pervade society and are redressed by the political system, depending on what political system we elect.

## Dr Robert Frosch FEng

It seems to me that population is a major controlling parameter. Running a sustainable world for a billion people would be quite different than for ten and certainly different than for a hundred and we would know how to do the former probably and probably don't have the faintest idea of how to do the latter. It's quite important that population should be a social parameter in the considerations.

It seems to me there are four fundamental ingredients to sustainability; materials, energy, system structure, and knowledge, which is the way in which we use the other three. We used the word consumption with regard to materials. We were rather vague about what we meant by consumption, and I would argue that from a physical point of view we do not ever consume materials at all. We do two things with them. There is a class of materials like metals which we use as the basic material and we don't consume it, we merely use it, we store it in products and then we restore those products and materials to the stream. Looking at the questions of efficiency of the metal stream in parts of US industry, it's extraordinarily high. Copper atoms don't get lost, they don't get consumed and they very seldom get dissipated so we need to think about that aspect of materials. The other thing we use in materials is their structure. The renewables are essentially the structuring of atoms into molecules and into systems. And that is an important point because in essence those things are reversible and reconstructible given a supply of energy at an economic value. The fundamental sustainability parameter from a physical point of view is going to be the availability of energy. We seldom use up water. We pollute it; we seldom take it apart. The issue of whether we can have it pure enough is an issue of energy, its availability, and its costs. And we keep coming back, as physicists and chemists and engineers, to the issues of energy and the provision of energy. I get nervous, therefore, when we start to talk about shifting from non-renewables to renewables because I think the problem of recycling non-renewables is probably simpler than the problem of dealing with the structure difficulties of renewables. In order to run a solar energy-driven renewable system, we will face a set of issues about land use and about the structure of the ecosystems in which we choose to grow the renewables. The first thing we are likely to do in that agricultural situation is to set about destroying a natural ecological structure. We need to understand how to do the engineering of ecological systems, what their structure is, what the nature of the complications are, and how we can begin to use them without necessarily destroying them. I am reminded of Francis Bacon's comment 'Nature to be commanded must be obeyed'. And I think we must literally take that in the sense of understanding the structures with which we are doing engineering and learning how they operate so that when we choose to use them as means of production we can use them in a way which is sustainable and not a way which is destructive.

## Sir John Knill FEng

When I face issues of this kind where I am dealing with a physical development, one has to have some form of guidance in one's mind with regard to Sustainable Development. Certainly the phrase intergenerational equity is the guide that I always use. I find it really rather robust in many ways, in at least developing a model in relation to any particular development. I realise there are uncertainties in such a predictive approach but you have to appreciate that I am a geologist and therefore I am not afraid of time. I'm certainly happy to think about time backwards! And if you can think about time backwards for several millennia it doesn't challenge you very much to think on a decadal basis forwards. Time is something that geologists think about so that is a starting point. But when you look at intergenerational equity it does enable you to look from the implications of a development, from the initial resource acquisition right the way through to decommissioning. The earlier discussion on decommissioning was really rather interesting. If one looks at the total life of developments I think that we have a very much more practical way to look to the future.

At the end of this meeting, we will have to carry away ideas within The Academy which can be converted to action. How can one translate all this at the level of the undergraduate? How can we train the undergraduate to think in relation to how Sustainable Development is applied? Or the young engineer facing a CAD screen and the hidden implications of cost and period of construction, as he manipulates that CAD screen in relation to a design. And therefore there needs to be clear guidance, both in education and in training. But it's not only a bottom-up process, it's top down in the sense that there have to be clear instructions from clients through the system as to how a particular development is going to be looked at, whether they even wish it to be viewed from a viewpoint of Sustainable Development. And in relation to planning applications and development proposals of different kinds, it would be valuable to see a model in each case which does take Sustainable Development into account. A good example of this is the re-evaluation of the Newbury by-pass which was carried out this year. There was suggested the possibility of a tunnel solution for all or part of the Newbury by-pass. There are no technical problems involved in such a solution, it's merely a question of cost. But there has never been any approach to the Newbury by-pass which does seriously take into account Sustainable Development. But again, in the background, we have to think very carefully about timing. Many engineering proposals take increasingly long periods of time to carry from the drawing board to the actual inception and the process of promotion through planning inquiries and all the other procedural steps is lengthy. I would hope, if Sustainable Development was seen to be more a part of the system, that there could be greater recognition at public level that there had been a responsible approach taken towards the design and planning of proposals of this kind. In that way, possible controversy and even confrontation could be minimised. Maybe Sustainable Development offers us one way in which we can see an opportunity to move more quickly from a concept to a reality.

## Sara Parkin

I have been tremendously impressed with the way the engineering profession has tackled this whole issue head on. My first involvement was in the Engineering Council conference in 1990 and I have subsequently been very interested in the way the whole process at a professional level has been tackled. I think there are three phases we are going through as far as the environment agenda is concerned.

The first phase was when people like me were screaming and shouting and tub thumping to get these issues on to the agenda. We've done that. Then there was a tremendously intense phase of policy development, an enormous number of ideas and practical solutions and engineers have had a massive input. We are on a sort of cusp of the next phase and that is making sense of that great potpourri of ideas, policies and solutions for people in general and for decision makers in particular. And so I think it is a very interesting phase in which we find ourselves.

I would however like to make one point about rationality and emotion, because again and again I have encountered the argument that these are opposites. If engineering and science put these two things head to head, history tells us that emotion will win. It is a matter of getting a balance between the two and recognising that most people are a mixture of the rational and the emotional. Decisions that are made from a rational point of view also have to be made, discussed and debated with people who are perhaps going to be taking a more emotional point of view. Inefficiency in the system may be a very important price that we pay for involving people. I would encourage you just to build in a little bit of inefficiency as part of that social acceptability of the various choices we have to make.

I'd also like to emphasise that Sustainable Development is a process much more than a philosophy. It is about people and about equity. Compromises have to be made and we in the developed countries actually have to say that we are going to use a lot less in our development and that the poor countries have to admit that they can't follow the same development paths as we can. If you are going to make that possible then there has to be that first step taken in the rich countries. We have to be a bit humble in the face of this whole process too. The actual systems that give us the weather and all the rest of it are so huge I strongly suspect, and indeed I hope, that we will never understand how they work. I do believe there has to be some sort of mystery left. Humility in front of the physical powers of the earth is very important for us because it also teaches us we can learn from them as well.

It is also very important to take your vision of what the future might be, not from an engineering perspective but from what people feel in their communities. That means, perhaps, using your neighbourhood engineering connections to get involved in the envisioning processes that are going on through Agenda 21 to see what it is that people want, what do they see as necessary in 2020. It is then for you to see how engineering can deliver that. I agree very much that the professional position of engineers should build trust in the word of engineers. We've seen the need for that with Brent Spar. We've seen that people don't trust government and they don't trust companies. There is an enormous opportunity for engineers as a profession to be able to provide the forum in which various voices that have a concern in a decision which involves an engineering solution can come together to make that decision. The profession should seek to broker the trust of people in what can often be very complex decisions.

## Chairman

I have a series of questions which have been handed in, the first from **Dr Glyn England FEng (Windcluster Ltd)**.

"We have heard a lot about what is being done and what needs to be done. We've heard less about the barriers which are handicapping progress. Could the panel suggest the main constraints to which we, as engineers and citizens, should be giving attention."

## Lord Tombs

I think the principal barriers to movements towards true sustainabilty are those of uncertainty, the inability to be very sure about what the measures should be or indeed what the cost/ benefit relationship is. We've been pretty good at the things where the precautionary principle comes in, for example the risks, in spite of the uncertainties, of a climate change are so great that it has been thought necessary internationally to try to restrict the growth of $CO_2$ in the atmosphere. And in areas like that where the imperative is clear, we have been fairly good at responding. In the optional areas where things are perhaps desirable or economically good we have been much less good, partly because of the availability of the analysis, partly the diffuse nature of Western governments. For example, subscribing to the UK policy for Sustainable Development are twelve separate departments and anyone who knows British government knows that is a remedy for inaction and internal committee making. We do suggest one or two things in the Select Committee which I hope will command the support of the Government. But I think the will is there in Government. The populace is, I think, prepared to be convinced of the need for sometimes demanding measures. We just have to be sure that we are standing on good ground in doing them and that we can with reasonable robustness demonstrate the worthwhileness of the actions either in planet preservation or in economic terms.

## Sara Parkin

I should just like to add the psychological barrier. As a species we are fairly conservative. When we change we like it to happen gradually rather than quickly and I think the language of change is very important. We should extend the notion of the precautionary principle and use words such as 'security, insurance'. People understand that sort of language and I think the way you talk about change is very important.

## Chairman

Of course rapid change challenges vested interests, it challenges commitment and investment and the whole fabric on which people have built their lives. Phasing in change at a rate that is sufficient for the environment but doesn't impose too large a stress on society, is crucial.

The next question is from **Donald Bruce, Director of the Society, Religion & Technology Project, Church of Scotland**: "A missing element in the debate is the unemployment dimension. Technology has been geared towards making people less necessary than to create employment. How we pursue sustainable economic development must also include the need to create more rather than less jobs. How can engineers make a difference? What should they be making that will create jobs and remain environmentally sustainable?"

## Sara Parkin

I think we need to de-link the notion of jobs from work. There is loads of work that needs to be done so we need to look at the way we distribute the pain, the joys and the rewards of that work. We have to look at ways of distinguishing the work that earns money from the work that is done voluntarily. This is especially relevant in underdeveloped countries because it's not going to be possible to deliver well being to people in underdeveloped countries through the same sort of employment systems we have, yet that is what is being promoted.

## Chairman

The people I have spoken to from developing countries always say "we start with one huge asset, we have a vast human resource we can develop". I think there is a dimension here of how to develop the human resource as a chief goal of society.

Now I have two linked questions. One is from **Dr Mike Yendell, Director, Special Projects, University of Strathclyde**: "There has been little discussion so far on the drivers for change. Engineers will deliver what companies need to develop sustainably. This will only happen when the capital markets put pressure on companies. Does the panel have confidence that accounting practice or fiscal policies will change in future years so that environmental externalities are taken in to account?" The second question is from **Rear Admiral William Rourke, Australian Academy of Technical Sciences and Engineering**: "In discussion on Session 2 it was suggested that the costs of environmental impacts could not be assessed and that there is no way of comparing the value of polar bears and buttercups. Would the panel agree that externalities and intangibles have to be addressed in some way that often involves an implicit valuation, and that it is a challenge to society to allow social costs and benefits to be broadly and reasonably assessed?"

## Dr Frosch

The thing I have learned most about accounting is that internal accounting for even the things that are obvious is not very good. I was in the Pentagon in the balmy days of cost effectiveness when Mr MacNamara was first there and we spent a great deal of time worrying about effectiveness of things. It gradually dawned on us that we knew a great deal more about effectiveness than we knew about costs. It was frequently quite impossible to tell from the accounting data what it was a project had cost after it was finished. Most accounting is done not by detail but by convention and it may be that the accounting of externalities will have to be by some agreed convention. I have relatively little faith in what is called contingent valuation, namely, 'lets go and ask the people what they would pay'. I think that we will have to go through a period of experimental valuation and have a kind of debate on what to do with polar bears and separately on what to do with buttercups. When we pose it as a major engineering and business question it looks daunting, but everyone does a daily exercise in mixed value evaluation in deciding how to run a personal budget, whether to eat a fancy dinner or buy a new necktie or something else. We have some sort of personal, internal algorithm for doing it. What we need to do is find some way to debate out how the internal algorithm gets turned into a social algorithm and that may not at first be a very good formal algorithm that we can agree on but perhaps a process by which we can learn to take these things into account, something that would eventually become an accounting system.

## Lord Tombs

I'd like to agree with that; we do make these decisions. We don't have a refrigerator because it's economic to have one, we have one because it's convenient to have one so we import all sorts of other notions into the economic valuation and we have to find a way of transferring that to the national psyche. On the earlier point, that of making provision or at least taking account, I think the signs are encouraging. Already the shock to some companies of having to decommission sites has focused the attention of accountants. It has come as rather a big surprise in a number of cases. The attention of industrialists is coming round very much to what might it cost us. It won't be very long before the accountants go overboard and want provision for everything and bankrupt companies in doing so if we're not careful. But the pendulum will swing to and fro and I think there will be a conscious recognition of these contingent costs which are lying there waiting to be recognised.

## Chairman

I think one of the things that has happened in the past 20 years is the amazing transformation of the debate; how a lot of things that were totally disregarded as unmentionable externalities are now brought right into the equation and taken very seriously.

## Sara Parkin

I think at the moment there is a feeling that it should be economists who help governments set their goals for Sustainable Development. I think that will change. Goals will be increasingly set by environmental scientists and they will then pull in economists and engineers to help society review the choices available to reach those goals.

## Chairman

Two more linked questions, the first from **John Plevin, Policy and Communications, NERC**:

"The developing world, fuelled by ever increasing populations, will be the major consumer of non-renewable resources in the future. Will this derail the plans of the developed world for a sustainable future? If yes, what must be done? What should the engineering profession do?"

The second question is from **Mr Maurice Laws, Chairman, Smallpeice Enterprises Ltd**: "What evidence can members of the panel cite to support the Conference optimism that a balance between resource consumption and sustainability can be achieved without some diminution in population aspirations?"

## Sir John Knill

I think that if one goes to the developing world what I find tremendously optimistic, certainly in the English language newspapers, is the appreciation of environmental issues. The *Straits Times* or the Indonesian English language paper often have a very high proportion of their content related to global , national and local environmental questions. I believe that many of the developing countries, actively involved in industrialisation, are very well aware of many of the issues that we are discussing. So I think that the answer to the first question is yes, I think that the developed world may well be destabilised but I think that the developing world is very conscious of what they are doing at the present time. At a conference in 1975 in Sao Paulo I had quite a strong debate about the activities within the Amazon Basin and I predicted then that the Amazon would be flowing red into the Atlantic by the year 2000. I believe that I am going to be wrong, I'm glad to say, but it was a very interesting debate because at that time the attitude was very much, by fellow geologists, that this is our country and we will choose to do what we like with it. That philosophy has changed quite significantly in Brazil over the intervening years so I think we are dealing with a much more understanding world than the question might seem to imply. As engineers what should we be doing about it? Well, my belief is that we should be guiding by example, in terms of our work in those countries as to the way forward. I think we should also be looking very much to the future in this country in solving problems which will themselves be translatable into other parts of the world which face now or will face in the future the problems that we have. One aspect in the developing world that possibly in the developed world we do not face at the moment is the problem of mega cities. In the increased population of the future, most of the increase is going to live in mega cities. And I believe one of the greatest questions is how those mega cities are going to operate, how they are going to develop and whether or not we are going to get enhanced disaster-type situations in environments of that particular type.

## Sara Parkin

There are two aspects to this. One is this idea that population is a distant problem. If you look at the population density of Africa you find that it's much better than the density in Europe. In fact if you take Europe, you'll find that this is the world region that is most densely populated and yet that is never thought of. What does it take to make the population of Europe function to the level it does? This was something that Jacques Delors pointed out in his white paper on Growth, Employment and Competition. In the final chapter he said that if you actually look at the resources that have to be brought in so that we can function, they are huge. We are very dependent on those countries where population is growing enormously and there will come a point where they will have to say that charity begins at home, we need those resources for ourselves. So I think we have to help other countries follow development patterns that don't compound the mistakes that we have made. So that's again where engineering comes in. How do you make Europe and the population it contains able to function on far, far less than the share of resources that it currently takes from the larger world.

## Chairman

That's a telling point. Remember that it took over a hundred years for the demographic transition in Western Europe to go through, for the falling death rates to be followed by the falling birth rates. It is going two or three times as rapidly in the developing world today, which is something nobody ever publicises. In parts of South East Asia the demographic transition is accomplished. It is proceeding rapidly in Central and South America and it is well under way even in Africa. So the population time bomb is, I think defusing itself. Give it another 30 or 40 years and we may well stabilise at a much lower world population than some of the gloomy stories suggested.

Now a question from **Dr Chris Elliott, Director, Smith System Engineering Ltd**: "Much of the discussion has revolved around ethical responsibilities of engineers. Where do those responsibilities end if they do? Is it enough for engineers to do their engineering professionally and responsibly according to the tasks as defined by their customers or should they take a lead in setting ethical standards?"

## Dr Frosch

I think there are two questions here. One is the relationship of the engineer to the customer, and the other embedded in it is the ethical aspect. I guess I have spent now 44 years peddling technology and doing R&D for customers and the main thing I have learned is that the customer is always wrong. That doesn't mean that you don't pay attention to the customer. It means that the customer's expressed desire is usually the customer's estimate of a solution and not the customer's problem. So the first ethical obligation is to engage in enough dialogue so that you can help define the question. I mean that in the literal sense of helping the customer uncover what is the desire or the need to be satisfied in the light of what an engineer or a scientist can actually do to deliver solutions. You are not only defining solutions, you ought to be helping to define the problem. I think it is an ethical responsibility to question the instruction you have been given. You may then end up being told to do it anyway and to answer the problem you have been given. You then have an ethical question as to whether you take the job or take the consequences and that can be painful and difficult but I think you have to consciously think about it in that way. We presumably are going to be the developers of the rational, system-related arguments but part of the ethics of doing that is that you be as clear as possible as to the assumptions that are going in to your statement of rationality so that can be part of the dialogue with the customer. Did the customer really intend that set of assumptions by the question that was asked? So I think in a way the ethical answer comes by insisting on the dialogue and on taking responsibility for the things that the engineer can do, which is to help define the problem and to help define rational solutions to the problem where rational is circumscribed by the assumptions that have to be understood by both parties.

## Chairman

The final written question comes from **John Davis FEng, retired former Head of Product and Marketing Development at Shell**: 'The rate of progress in Sustainable Development depends, as Sir Robin Ibbs said, on engineering enterprise combined with financial enterprise. Lloyds Bank lenders are guided in their judgements by a manual which reflects the Bank's view only. It may or may not correspond with what is in the public interest and could possibly inhibit progress. Is there now a need to begin to develop a common framework of guidelines in which engineers can contribute a critical input as to what is technically feasible?

## Lord Tombs

I start from the somewhat old fashioned point of view that Lloyds Bank's job is to run its bank not the whole of society. It has a position in society which it has to observe and it has to behave responsibly. But the real lead for environmental improvement has to be led by society, that is to say by government through either fiscal or regulatory measures and people have to behave within that framework in a proper, thoughtful and responsible way. But I don't think it's for Lloyds Bank or any bank or any other institution to try to carry the burdens of society.

## Sir John Knill

We do need guidelines and I think we need guidelines at different levels. We need them certainly at university level, possibly sixth form level, and certainly in the development of young engineers as to how they apply the practice of Sustainable Development on a day to day basis and how that is converted into the implications in terms of cost, time scale, and everything else that is associated with it.

## Sara Parkin

Well, I am a big fan of guidelines but I think it is important that they don't get set in stone. Guidelines must be continually evolving because, as knowledge changes and our understanding changes, they must change along with them. Otherwise they become dangerous. I think that the process by which Lloyd's Bank arrived at their guidelines will come increasingly under scrutiny. I am not quite sure who they consulted to produce their guidelines that influence who they lend money to. But with the idea of liability engaging not just the people who manufactured something or got involved with a process but with whoever lent them money and whoever insured it, I think you will find insurance companies will want to know that guidelines on lending, like guidelines on engineering processes and other manufacturing processes, have been put together by a very wide consultative process.

## Chairman

Can I now invite questions from the floor?

## Professor Anthony Kelly CBE FEng FRS University of Cambridge

I hoped this session would give specific guidelines but the only one we have had is 'shout louder' so thank you for that. I would like to comment on what Robert Frosch said, which is very, very important. Metals are not consumed, they are merely used and they remain in the system, exactly the same as nitrogen which is not consumed. It's taken from the air, it is used, some of it is fixed and then it goes back. So there is a link between normal engineering and the biological systems. We should not talk of cradle to grave except for renewable sources of energy. We should think of conception to resurrection and go on and on and on. And I think it would help enormously if we stopped using the words cradle to grave. I'm not quite sure what to put in place of conception. There are various rival words I could use but it is resurrection we are talking about and only for non-renewable sources of energy is it cradle to grave.

## Dr Frosch

I just want to say that some people are simply saying in industrial circles 'cradle to cradle'.

## (Name inaudible)

I have had the privilege from industry in helping to develop science and technology education. Taking Lord Tombs' comment about influencing the national psyche and also his health warning about the uncertainties, there really is a difficult problem of how you introduce environmental teaching into schools with so many uncertainties and it lays it wide open to various external groups to come with subversive and unbalanced approaches. It is interesting, that although this conference is about Sustainable Development, and in fact perhaps we are borrowing from our grandchildren, that this aspect has never come up in this Conference. I think one action point for The Academy is to think about how to help the process started by John Gummer and Gillian Shepherd of introducing environmental teaching into the schools. Uncertainty is an open door for misleading young people who perhaps will approach it with a rational basis.

## Sara Parkin

Yes, this is extremely important. Someone did a survey on the environmental teaching packs that are put into schools by various organisations including, I think, the engineering profession. They came up with 140 or so guidelines. How teachers could make sense of all this, I don't know! One of the most important things would be staff training in environmental literacy and I gather that the Department for Education and Employment and the Department of the Environment are hoping to hold a conference at the beginning of next year which will look at a review of the Toyne report. It is also important to think of higher and further education. One thing The Academy and perhaps the new Engineering Council might consider is looking very hard at engineering education and whether just a bolt-on environmental module is enough or whether the whole of engineering education should be remodelled to address Sustainable Development, and the problems of it. How can engineering contribute to the solution so that you are actually training the engineers of the next century? I am involved in setting up a scholarship programme at the moment for young people at graduate level who have a commitment to sustainability and leadership potential. This is going to be based on placements in six different sectors including business, an environmental pressure group, politics, the media, even the Treasury. And the excitement that this whole programme has generated because they will be given the chance to see first hand where the opportunities and the barriers lie. They will be able to build up contacts and knowledge of how things work in other sectors and everyone I have spoken to said "these are the people we want to employ, we can train them in the specific needs of our company or our local authority, but we can't train them in understanding how the world works and having this broad range of contacts".

## Lord Tombs

Let me just make a comment about the uncertainty which the questioner seemed to think would make teaching more difficult. Life is full of uncertainties. None of us know when we are going to die, we none of us know what the weather is going to be tomorrow despite the best efforts of the Met. Office. I just think it is very important that we acknowledge the uncertainties in the environmental area, that politicians and the public should be discouraged from expecting certain answers and that we should say when we don't know.

## Professor Tony Ridley CBE FEng

Has this conference actually made a difference? And if The Academy met tomorrow morning what is the first thing you would ask us to do?

## Dr Frosch

I can only say what process we have been trying to go through in the US National Academy of Engineering for the past five or six years. We have assumed that we would not do the job with a single meeting. And so we have had a sequence of meetings on slightly different pieces of the agenda. The invited participants were a kind of a rolling, changing group of people so that we have had a core of people who have been interested in the subject. We've put it under the rubric of industrial ecology, and so we have got a slowly expanding group of people, industrial, academic and government who are interested. We can use both the papers and the discussion to produce a publication which also expands the audience so that we try to make a difference by developing the subject in a series of dialogues, by expanding the group that's interested and by some publications.

## Sara Parkin

We have talked about education and the ability of the profession to operate as a profession, as an independent authority with the power to lobby the Government. I'd like to add to that the need for the profession to make much more intimate links between itself and ordinary people so that they can perceive engineers as being main contributors to the whole Sustainable Development debate and indeed the practical solutions. I think that means looking at practical examples that are happening now. Not what could engineers do, or what they should do, but what they are doing now. Then market it in a popular way for ordinary people.

## David Cope UK CEED

It is more of an observation but I am grateful that an economist gets the last word here. It was really a comment about barriers but it also related to remarks that Sir John Knill and Lord Tombs made about equity. Just very quickly to share with you some ongoing work that a group of political economists are doing at Cambridge. Certainly we cannot find any principle within Sustainable Development which says that equity within generations is necessary for the achievement of Sustainable Development. It may be a desirable option but it's not actually necessary. It's the intergenerational dimension which is the key to Sustainable Development. We have been checking that by looking historically at societies which have over long periods of time been sustainable, they've lived within the constraints that existed at the time, like pre-Hispanic America, Pharonic Egypt, and so on. The one characteristic all those societies shared was that they were all what economists call consumptionist societies. In other words consumption was strictly controlled, and even if you actually had access to the means of resources you could not necessarily consume unless you belonged to a certain group. Now this, I am afraid we are concluding, has some implications for the relationship between Sustainable Development and Western representative democracy. And in some ways it may be the case that unless we can ratchet back representative democracy Sustainable Development, in terms of the transfer of resources to future generations, may actually be an even greater challenge than we think. I know this is highly controversial but I just thought I would share with you the results of our latest piece of research.

## Chairman

I think we will all want to read that report very carefully and very analytically but it's a good note to end on. I thank everyone who has taken part. I have pleasure in returning the chair to the President.

Sir  William Barlow FEng

President

The Royal Academy of Engineering

I do not propose to give you another summary after Sir Martin's masterly summary earlier on. I made a note, Sir Martin, about your eight points and the first one, "shout louder", is something I am in the habit of doing, but the other seven I find a bit more difficult. And as far as Tony Ridley is concerned, what will The Academy be doing? I want to tell you of some of the things which following this conference need our attention.

We began the Conference by looking at what society expects from engineers in the pursuit of Sustainable Development under a number of headings. First, I would say that engineers can provide information to assist in choices of technology and decisions that involve complex trade offs or conflicts of interests. For example, the use of life cycle inventory, described in the paper by Peter White, is one of the tools we now have and we must constantly put it across to a wide public as an example of what can be done. Another example could be the need for rational analysis of transport systems discussed by Christopher Elliott.

The second point to consider is integration because engineers can only make a useful contribution to the Sustainable Development debate if our intervention is made on a solid understanding of how engineering integrates with the broader environmental, ethical and political issues at stake. I should add here that recently the four British Academies, The Royal Society, The British Academy, The Conference of Royal Medical Colleges and our Academy have formed a group called the National Academies Policy Advisory Group to consider some major issues, taking into account medical, ethical and political opinion so that it is not just a case of engineers banging away without being challenged.

The third important thing that we can offer is innovation to develop the products and processes that will both meet the environmental targets specified by society, while being practical and economic. I was pleased that Sir Ronald Hampel was optimistic of our ability to innovate our way out of trouble and of course he gave a wonderful example from his own company of the KLEA range of products which won the MacRobert award last year and which will replace CFCs and HCFCs in refrigeration and air conditioning. That was a wonderful innovation which was duly rewarded and we can do a lot of good by rewarding other good examples as and when they come up for appraisal.

I told you at the beginning of the conference that there were a lot of business opportunities in this whole environmental concern. Both our political speakers drew attention to this. We all quoted big figures, they are very big figures, and like all the other forecasts we spoke of they will be wrong. But that does not matter. The main thing is to get people convinced that there is a whole new raft of businesses which can be built up in this scene. There is nothing wrong in making profit from good engineering in this sort of activity.

Another thing we have constantly got to do, and Sara Parkin referred to the excellent work the Engineering Council is doing on this, is to enhance the attractiveness of the engineering profession in the minds of young people who have concerns about the environment. By explaining what engineers can do to help the environment, I think we can interest them and give them a challenging opportunity.

There are some important drivers in ensuring that engineers take a full part in the debate. The Academy has recognised these and has Sustainable Development as a core theme in its

Corporate Plan. But as we are not a big organisation (there are only 1000 Fellows) with limited financial sources, our Corporate Plan is very carefully honed down to a few major issues and Sustainable Development is one of them. This Conference marks only the beginning of a process of events and arrangements and activities to galvanize engineers into action. Joan Ruddock said engineers probably lack any identity in the mind of the average citizen. Well, I often say that there is nothing hurts like the truth. But it is a challenge for us and not everyone thinks like that. I was pleased to hear David Worskett express his great confidence in us. We need to have confidence in our own ability and we need to get ourselves into the action confident that we can do things to help.

There are a few more specific actions that we shall take. We shall insist that engineers are represented in the various government panels and working groups. We had twenty eight Fellows on the Technology Foresight panels. We were there as of right in all those great exercises and we shall continue to insist that we are. We have links into the UK Round Table on Sustainable Development and will ensure that those links are used as a means of communication. We have important links in Europe. Basil Butler, one of our Vice-Presidents, is the Chairman of Euro-CASE, which advises the European Commission on matters of engineering and science. We are founder members of the Council of Academies of Engineering and Technical Sciences conditioning engineers to think about health, safety and environment right from the start.

An understanding of the important role of engineering in producing solutions to environmental problems in the context in which engineers operate should be a fundamental part of an engineer's education. We have heard our panellists say that and it is the intention of The Academy to do all we can to see that this happens. We might find scope to widen the remit of The Academy's design professorships. We have 92 visiting professors around the various universities in the country and it could well be that we could widen the remit of those and appoint some who could help very much on this scene. There are Clean Technology Studentships and we can perhaps do more in that direction; that needs to be explored.

This Conference builds on a very successful half day meeting in March 1994 *Signposting the Sustainable Development Strategy* and the momentum has increased very greatly since then. We intend, in The Academy, in answer to the various questions posed, to continue with a sequence of events providing platforms to stimulate engineering contributions to Sustainable Development. After this conference the organisers will be following up on the many points which have been made in the last two days. The quality of the talks and discussions has been very high and I for one feel very much better informed as a result of them.

I do want to thank the speakers who have been of the highest quality for the effort and thought and time they have put into our conference and stimulating us. I also want to thank the sponsors who provided heavy financial support to make this conference possible. I want to thank too the organising committee under Jim McQuaid who worked hard and long to put it all together. I also thank Christa Langan and her staff from The Academy for doing all the detailed work to put it together.

I assure you that the Academy will pursue vigorously the ideas put forward at this conference and will have a lot of follow-up meetings of various sizes and types. You will be hearing from us soon. Engineers will turn the vision of Sustainable Development into reality in many many ways. Dame Rachel said it for us: "Engineers must take centre stage, don't be afraid". I think she is quite right to exhort us to take centre stage and not to be afraid to do so. And that's what I would like to see The Academy encourage the whole of the engineering profession to do. Fortunately the Engineering Council is on the same wavelength. They have 250,000 members so with their weight and our enthusiasm I think we can make a lot faster progress than we have in the past. I hope The Academy has done something useful to stimulate engineers to play their part in this very important scene.